EXTENDING
MATHEMATICAL
ABILITY

Through Interactive
Whole Class Teaching

EXTENDING MATHEMATICAL ABILITY

Through Interactive Whole Class Teaching

David Fielker

Hodder & Stoughton

A MEMBER OF THE HODDER HEADLINE GROUP

To the children I have taught,
from whom I have learnt so much.

British Library Cataloguing in Publication Data
A catalogue entry for this title is available from the British Library

ISBN 0 340 68012 1

First published 1997
Impression number   10   9   8   7   6   5   4   3   2   1
Year   1999   1998   1997   1997

Typeset by Multiplex Techniques, Orpington, Kent.
Printed in Great Britain for Hodder & Stoughton Educational, a division of Hodder Headline Plc, 338 Euston Road, London NW1 3BH, Scotprint Ltd, Musselburgh, Scotland.

Contents

THIS BOOK IS FOR:

- the teacher who is worried about catering for a wide range of ability in mathematics, particularly the brighter pupils

- the teacher who is dissatisfied with the routine of textual schemes, and wants to do something more relevant

- the co-ordinator of mathematics who wants to assist colleagues in the improvement of their teaching

- the advisor or other in-service provider who wishes to provide teachers with techniques and strategies for change

- anyone organising special mathematical activities for gifted children

INTRODUCTION

I was about to work with a group of 10-year-olds using calculators. The teacher said, 'Do you mind if I put Sean with them? He's only nine, but I think he's bright.'

I worked through the activity described on p. 133 to the stage where I asked what I had to square in order to get 10. The 10-year-olds were busy squaring 3, 3.1, 3.2 etc. to see whether they could get 10.

Sean merely said, '3.1622776.'

'How did you get that?' I asked.

'I pressed 10, then this square root button,' he replied.

'I see,' I said. 'And when you square that, you get 10, do you?'

Sean squared it by pressing 'x, =', and got 9.9999996.

'That's not 10, is it?' I suggested.

'No,' said Sean, 'but that's the nearest you can get on this calculator. You haven't got enough digits.'

'Oh. How near is it?' I asked.

'Four ten-millionths,' said Sean immediately.
At the end of the session I said to his teacher, 'Yes, I think he *is* bright!'

It is not often we have someone like Sean in our classrooms. When we do, do we perhaps wonder where he learned these things that we did not teach him? Somehow children learn bits of mathematics without us, perhaps from their parents or older friends, perhaps in this case merely by playing around with a calculator and asking a few questions.

We should perhaps view this as a good thing. Why should children be restricted in their knowledge and understanding by our lessons, or indeed by *our* knowledge and understanding? It is easy to panic and worry about how *we* are going to cope with a situation in which a 9-year-old may know more mathematics than we do, rather than rejoice in the fact that our own knowledge is not holding him back.

Even if we feel confident enough to cope mathematically, we may feel that it is an *administrative* inconvenience. How can we provide suitable work for Sean and one or two other bright children when the rest of the class are at a more normal level for their age group and we are busy coping with the latter?

(Adam and Ben at the age of six used to tidy up the stock cupboard on Friday afternoons. That way their teacher felt they would not get too far ahead of the rest of the class!)

Although we realise that we have a wide spread of ability in our classes, sometimes we worry far more about those at the lower end of the scale. We spend a lot of energy and time giving help to those with learning difficulties. But bright children are a different sort of problem, for a variety of reasons. One has only to compare the wealth of written material, the extra resources – when we can afford them – and the subject associations devoted to children with learning difficulties, with the paucity of similar efforts we make for the bright, who in fact are also children with special needs.

This book is I hope more than just a handbook for teaching mathematics to bright children. It discusses how one can try to cope with a wide range of mathematical ability in a classroom, but with special reference to the brighter ones. It shows how to present activities that will stretch them, at the same time as providing material suitable for everyone. It also discusses the merits of various strategies for giving bright children special attention in mathematics.

The actual mathematical activities outlined are by no means a comprehensive list that will take you through the year. They are only a *sample*, chosen to illustrate a variety of ideas about ways of teaching and organising mathematics. They are restricted in scope anyway by the nature of this book, but what is important is not just the mathematics but the methods by which it is presented. These methods are in fact not just for the bright children: they are intended for everyone, and they are offered as a sensible and profitable way of teaching mathematics. It just so happens that it is also a way in which children of all abilities can work at the same situation.

A 10-year-old Turkish girl who had joined the class two weeks earlier had hardly had time to learn any English. The class was working on the same problem as Sean's group, presented in the form

$$\square \times \square = 10$$

where the same number was to go into each box. Like Sean, while the rest of the class was working away at trial and error, she entered 10 into her calculator and pressed the square root button.

I crossed the language barrier by giving her a further problem.

$$\square \times \square \times \square = 10$$

That took her a little longer, but the rest of the class was still working at the square root problem. Without thinking too carefully, I gave her

$$\square \times \square \times \square \times \square = 10.$$

She entered 10 into her calculator and pressed the square root button twice!!

Section A discusses some of the mainly organisational problems of coping with a range of mathematical ability in a classroom, and some ways of dealing with these.

Section B is mainly concerned with ways of finding suitable problems to present to mixed classes.

Section C presents a selection of suitable ideas in each main area of the mathematics syllabus, with a full discussion of what is involved.

SECTION A

ORGANISING MATHEMATICS FOR EVERYONE

This section is divided into three chapters:

CHAPTER 1
Some concerns

CHAPTER 2
Options

CHAPTER 3
Another approach

SOME CONCERNS

This chapter discusses a wide range of considerations in respect of children who are 'gifted' in mathematics. Some of these are directly relevant to teachers, and some are not. The aim is to clear out of the way those items that may not be relevant, and to discuss in more detail those that are.

The headings that follow (though not the commentary) are taken from some which appeared on a paper produced for a Working Group on Mathematics for Gifted Students which took place during the Eighth International Congress on Mathematical Education in Seville in 1996. The headings provide a convenient list of questions (explicit or implicit) to be discussed, except that they were framed for the international setting of the congress. Here I have tried to put my comments in a more local context.

THE PHENOMENON OF 'GIFTEDNESS'

There is much concern in some circles about the nature and identification of mathematical giftedness. Ability at mathematics is not always easy to recognise. Sometimes it is fairly obvious, as in the case of the two children described in the introduction, although on each occasion described there, only a small sample of ability was revealed. It is also interesting to note the tentativeness of Sean's teacher: 'I *think* he's bright!'

At the other extreme, we must be aware of those few bright children who appear *not* to be good at mathematics, but are in fact bored to death, and do not think that the trivial material being presented to them is worth bothering about.

In between, we have a more complex situation.

I have spent many years giving 'demonstration' lessons on teachers' courses, or in other people's classrooms. Whenever the class teacher is present it is quite common for them to comment on one or two children, either those who they thought were good at mathematics but who suddenly now appeared not to be, or those who were normally poor at it but now suddenly shone!

The different approach of my lessons concerned partly the type of material presented, but mainly a quite contrasting teaching style, in which the focus was on the children's ideas rather than on any fixed agenda in the teacher's mind. This difference in style apparently affected these particular few children in one of two ways. For those used to being good at a certain type of mathematics, the sudden demands of being asked to contribute their own ideas was too unsettling. On the other hand, those same demands appeared to release some energy in others who now found that they did have ideas to offer.

Discussion of ideas is also more *verbal* than is calculation with numbers. This means that some children, who generally appear to be good at mathematics but poor at language, can find it difficult to cope even with numerical ideas if the concentration is on description and explanation rather than just on calculation.

There are children who revel in mathematics of the routine nature characteristic of many textbooks or workcards, where their good memories enable them to achieve a lot of correct answers, and they are therefore considered to be bright. In a lesson where they are asked to rely less on memory and more on logical thinking, however, they sometimes flounder.

Another difference in my own lessons is that many of the activities were based on *spatial* problems. Some children lean either towards spatial or towards numerical ability. I have met children who normally consider themselves to be good at the mainly numerical mathematics they have been required to do, who are suddenly lost in a geometrical situation; and I have met those who have always had trouble with number, yet suddenly blossom when dealing with spatial ideas.

So, definitions are complex, and identification is difficult. One immediate message is that a wide variety of types of mathematical activity is more likely to give opportunities for *all* children to achieve something.

(One head teacher, with cheerful cynicism, told me that in her school, children were gifted mathematically if their grandparents said they were!)

APPROACHES TO THE IDENTIFICATION AND FOSTERING OF MATHEMATICAL GIFTEDNESS WITHIN EDUCATIONAL SYSTEMS

It emerged in Seville that countries varied in the way they treated mathematically gifted children, from those that set up special institutions for them, to those that maintained a strictly egalitarian approach.

There are no special institutions in the UK. However, there have been experiments with Saturday morning clubs, special residential weekends, and other ways of getting pupils from different schools together in order to foster an interest in mathematics. There are advantages for such activities. They enable an extended period of contiguous time to be spent on mathematics, so that longer problems can be dealt with uninterrupted. These programmes are usually staffed by tutors or teachers who have some specialism in the teaching of mathematics. Above all, they enable bright children – if they are the ones for whom the activity is provided – to work with their peers, and thus to feel for once that they are not in some way odd or unusual.

Being bright academically can be a lonely state, resented rather than admired by one's fellow pupils. For some reason or other, children have always tended to respect and value prowess at physical activity, yet are threatened by academic superiority. In an environment that has been specially set up, however, a bright child can be valued by other, equally bright children. In a normal classroom, bright children can learn that it is not tactful to flaunt one's brightness; indeed, they may try to hide it for fear of being unpopular. A teacher has to be aware of the social and emotional aspects of brightness, and needs to handle all situations with care.

Otherwise, the general problem of how to deal with bright children for most primary schools is one of organisation. We can put children into classes by streaming, by setting or by mixed ability. Usually there is a general school policy about whether classes are mixed, as is more traditional, or streamed according to general ability; so it is then a question of whether one sets for mathematics, i.e. whether there is streaming according to mathematical ability just for mathematics lessons. We have to consider whether it is going to be policy to do this. And if the purpose is to isolate a group of mathematically gifted children, then we have to know if there are going to be enough of them to make such a group feasible.

There are some obvious *administrative* advantages in having a more coherent group of children. In a traditional mode of teaching one can arrange the same work for them all rather than have to provide different material for different abilities, and explanations will tend to be appreciated by everyone without the need to spend more time with the less able. Furthermore, where a discussion takes place it will have a better chance of carrying everyone with it, with less chance of the less able being lost, or of the more able being bored.

However, I say 'more coherent' rather than just 'coherent' because even a setted class has a surprising range of ability. Even one that begins as an apparently coherent group can soon throw up 'tails' at both ends of the spectrum.

In any case, as I indicated in the last section, mathematical ability, at whatever level, can be far more complex than one unified measurable quantity, and a supposedly coherent group based on numerical ability may diverge considerably in a spatial context, or vice versa.

One consideration in setting for mathematics, therefore, is again how we *identify* mathematical ability. Tests vary widely in their capacity to assess mathematics as a whole, or different branches of it, and they tend not to assess other aspects, like the ability to discuss, to explain, to present an argument, to appreciate the arguments of others or to have ideas!

Even without being cynical, one could say that most tests merely test the ability to do well on tests!

WHAT MATHEMATICS SHOULD THE GIFTED BE TAUGHT, AND HOW?

The Seville paper presented three options about mathematics for the gifted:

1   faster (the same content in less time)
2   more (more content in the same time)
3   deeper (basically the same content but more depth)

It is hard to see the difference between the first two! However, they represent an option typified by those secondary schools who used to put a top stream in for GCSE examinations a year early (in order, as one head of department once put it to me, 'to get it out of the way!'). The option now for primary schools is to move brighter children up through the levels of the National Curriculum.

One can see that this option requires those children to be working on different topics from the rest of the class, and this raises the administrative problems discussed above; again setting would make this arrangement far easier to manage.

Notwithstanding the pressures of national testing and league tables, we can at least consider possible objections to this option of acceleration through the curriculum.

There are of course *administrative* problems to do with both present and future organisation. The diversity involved already causes some problems when we begin the process of acceleration. If pupils get ahead on the curriculum at an early stage, then they will gradually get even further ahead at later stages. Then the range of achievement in a top set, in terms of topics covered, will become even greater. Subsequent organisations will become even more difficult to arrange. Secondary schools may not be either willing or able to continue such differentiation.

However, even though the administrative problems of necessity deserve some consideration, what is more important in an ideal world is a consideration of the *educational* aspects of acceleration.

First, is acceleration desirable?

This is hard to answer. There appears to be no evidence of acceleration doing children harm, but nor is there evidence that it does them any good. *In fact, they do not learn more about mathematics this way. What they do is merely learn the same mathematics sooner.* This does not seem to fulfil the needs of the more able, who deserve something better.

In the UK since the late 1940s it has been rare for bright children to be moved up the school to work with children in an older year group. This practice is more common in the USA. The objection here is not only that such children are merely doing the same work earlier, but that there are other dangers.

One is that although all the children in any class may be working on the same topics, the class is now a mixture of bright children and perhaps duller ones, so that any homogeneity is in the material to be studied, rather than in the type of children studying it. This does not really solve the problem of the range of ability at all.

A second danger is to do with maturity. Younger children may be brighter, but they do not mix easily with children who are possibly physically, socially and emotionally more mature.

A third danger is the resentment felt by ordinary or less able pupils in a class where younger children are appearing to do better, which will be felt even more than the resentment felt by children of the same age, as indicated earlier. The consequent social and emotional problems could be correspondingly greater.

Second, is acceleration necessary?

It may be necessary for those teachers who do not know what else to do other than to proceed with the readily available material in the scheme they are using. I state this not so much as a criticism of teachers, but as a criticism of schemes, which in general assume a linear approach to mathematics, in which all pupils follow the same course as far as they can. (This is also a criticism of the National Curriculum, which assumes the same thing.)

It is also perhaps a criticism of current provision for in-service education, where *continual* support for teachers, of the type that used to be provided by teachers' centres, and by mathematics centres in particular, is no longer available.

Given the right level of support, there is no reason why the third option indicated above, i.e. a *deeper* consideration of mathematics, should not be on offer. This book is by no means a replacement for the continual support which an adequate level of in-service provision would give. However, it is hoped that it will help to provide a basis for such provision, or at least some sort of aid in the absence of it.

TEACHERS OF MATHEMATICALLY GIFTED PUPILS

The National Curriculum introduced into the primary school a greater concentration on subject-oriented teaching, and many new topics in subjects such as mathematics and science. Consequently, there has been some discussion of whether primary-school teachers, like their secondary-school colleagues, should move towards subject specialism more widely than just in the traditional specialist areas like physical education and music.

Unless or until this happens, most primary teachers will continue to teach most subjects to their own classes, including mathematics. The question of whether children with special ability in mathematics should have specialist mathematics teachers only arises in those few schools which can afford the staffing and organisation to cope with this provision.

If staffing levels allow it, and if suitable teachers are available, then there are ways of providing extra stimulation for gifted pupils. I have been lucky enough for a couple of years to work part-time in a school where my sole job was to provide such extra stimulation. I have done this in two ways.

For some of the older children, I have been timetabled to take small groups of children for 'extra mathematics'. These groups have been self-selecting. The course was advertised as being more difficult. Pupils could opt for it, and if they found it was too difficult for them they could leave, without any stigma being attached to them. The material was carefully chosen to be something different from the normal syllabus, yet it covered or used many of the same ideas, and occasionally anticipated some further work.

For younger children, I have been timetabled one lesson a week to do 'enrichment mathematics'. Here I have similarly been able to introduce different topics, but I have also presented activities that enhance the children's normal work.

Many of the ideas I have worked on are described in this book.

However, this facility is a luxury available to few schools. This book is therefore directed mainly to the *classroom* teacher of mathematics, and aims to offer guidance as to how to manage a normal class in which there happen to be some children who show signs of mathematical giftedness.

2

OPTIONS

In this chapter, we look critically at the range of options open to a classroom teacher in organising work in mathematics in a mixed classroom ...

THE TRADITIONAL LINEAR SCHEME

If you use a textbook or any similarly structured course, then you have various ways of adapting it to the different rates at which pupils in your class will work. To start with, you may choose (1) to let all children progress through the book at their own pace, or (2) to try to keep them together.

1   If children all proceed at different paces through the book, then you will have administrative problems coping with a situation in which they are all doing different things. You may be relying on a scheme which is sufficiently well written and designed to enable most children to work on their own, and be devoting most of your time to helping the less able. Note that this probably means that you are neglecting the needs of the others, particularly the most able children.

It may also mean that most children are working on their own, or at best in pairs or small groups, so that there is little or no opportunity for a class discussion: that would be meaningless since the children are working on different topics.

In addition, by the end of the year, the quicker children may have finished the book, while the slower ones are still near the beginning. This means that there are topics towards the end of the book that many children have not covered, even though they may quite easily have coped with them. (In some schemes, for instance, it is the geometrical topics that appear towards the end, and there are then children who never get around to any geometry, even though they may have been able to cope with it better than with other topics!)

2   About the only way of keeping children together throughout a book is if they start each section together. The trouble is that whenever you decide to move them all on to the next section, there will be some who will have finished the previous one, but others who will not.

There are various ways of not satisfying everybody! You may have planned how you are going to get through the book by the end of the year, and will move on when your plan has determined it is time to do so. You may be more flexible, but choices are still difficult. You can move on when the quickest children are ready, so that they are the only ones who fully benefit from the scheme, or you may wait until most of the children are ready, in the mean time keeping those who finish early happy by giving them something extra in mathematics, or perhaps something entirely different!

The big danger here is the same one as before: that the less able never finish anything, only now this happens more often.

Whether you choose option 1 or 2, there is, incidentally, a curious effect which mathematics textbooks have on children, especially if they are concerned about the progress through it that we have been discussing. I was once visiting a class of 9-year-olds, and as I began to wander around the room I said to several children, 'What are you doing?'

Some said, 'Maths.'

I replied, 'Yes, I know it's maths; this is a maths lesson. What are you doing?'

I then got the sort of reply I received from most of the others: 'I'm on page 36,' or 'I've just finished number 7.'

In other words, they did not tell me *what they were doing*, but *where they were up to*. Just like a teacher worried about keeping them all together, they were more concerned with their pace through the book than with the mathematics itself!

In other classes which did not use textbooks or workcards, when I asked them what they were doing, they actually told me: 'I'm seeing how many triangles I can make on this 9-pin geoboard,' or 'I'm finding out which score turns up most when I throw two dice.'

THE MULTI-TRACK COURSE

Some schemes have been specifically designed as, say, three-part schemes, with three different texts, each covering more or less the same ground, but at different levels of difficulty. An alternative is to use entirely different schemes for children of different ability. This method of organisation looks simple enough, and can look as if it will work more successfully than having everyone using the same scheme, but it does have some disadvantages.

Allocating children to separate schemes according to ability is virtually the same process as streaming or setting them, except that if you keep them within the same class then the children are perhaps even more conscious of who is on which scheme. If you are going to do this, you may just as well stream the children, or set them for mathematics.

It still makes it difficult to do any class work altogether, because the pupils are even more likely to be working on different topics. There will also be the same troubles over the varying rates at which pupils work through each of the schemes, even if you think it will not be quite as varied as it would have been with a single textbook. Once started on a particular scheme, it is difficult for pupils to change schemes if it turns out that they are finding the work too easy or too difficult. Furthermore, this arrangement does not cater for those children who, for instance, are good at number work and poor at spatial work, or vice versa.

It also makes it even more difficult for the teacher to cope with individual difficulties. It is probably a delusion that tailoring the course to the pupil in this way makes such help less necessary. For some children the very fact that they are using a textbook is the difficulty, as much as the standard of work, and it will still be those on the 'lowest' course who will be needing the most attention. Anyway, now there is more variety in the classroom with which the teacher has to deal, since the pupils will be at varying places in three schemes rather than just one!

In short, it could be that any doubtful advantages in having different schemes for different abilities are far outweighed by their disadvantages.

THE INDIVIDUALISED SCHEME

Individualised schemes are usually based on complicated systems of workcards, either commercially produced or home-made. Few teachers these days have time to prepare their own, and commercial ones tend to be expensive if they are produced with an individualised scheme in mind. (I discount those workcard schemes which are really pages of textbooks stuck onto cards; this actually used to happen!) So, expense or time may make this option a non-starter, but at least we can discuss the ideas involved here to see what we can gain from them, positively or negatively.

The idea in something like the SMILE (Secondary Mathematics Individualised Learning Experiment) secondary scheme is that the teacher regularly prepares for each pupil a set of, say, eight cards on which to work. This is the 'individualised' feature of the scheme, because the new sets which are allocated ideally depend on the individual capabilities of the pupils, what they last did, and generally on what is appropriate for them. Possibly each pupil is encouraged to work at some of the cards with one or more others, so that 'individualised' applies to each pupil's course rather than implying that work is done in isolation.

SMILE had some particular advantages in its early days because it was basically not a commercial scheme available to everyone, but was written by the teachers in the schools which were using it in order to suit themselves, and was continually revised, updated and augmented. It also tried to make full use of a wide range of resources: computers, calculators, tape recorders, television, reference books, materials etc.

However, I used to find some particular disadvantages in some SMILE classrooms, and in other classrooms where similar schemes were in operation.

The teacher can find it difficult to occupy a role other than that of manager, allocating sets of cards, marking test cards, directing pupils to resources, and never actually teaching! One cause of this was that the cards themselves were so self-sufficient, in the sense that the pupils always knew exactly what to do and never needed any help!

This sounds like the perfect situation, but I have serious worries. These are due to what I call the 'tried and tested in the classroom' syndrome, a slogan that used to be seen in the advertising for some commercial schemes, and it works like this. Draft cards are tried out in a number of pilot classrooms. The pupils experience a lot of difficulties and ask a lot of questions. The feedback is received by the authors, and the cards are rewritten. This process is gone through once or twice more, with fewer and fewer queries experienced from the pupils. When there are hardly any questions at all and most pupils understand exactly what to do, the cards are published.

My objection is that if the cards have become so undemanding, I doubt whether the children are learning any mathematics!

There can be some advantages in using a *good* set of workcards in this way, but the best ones I have seen were some of the home-made ones. What is really important is not the system but the quality of what one sees on the card or the page.

An overall disadvantage is one of all printed matter, commercial or home-made: the printed word becomes the sole stimulus, and determines what happens, regardless of how a teacher, or in the following case a visitor, tries to encourage something more general.

> **John and Stephen had a card on *Tangrams*, and they had all the pieces on their table.**
> **'Will they make a square?' I asked. John assembled them immediately.**

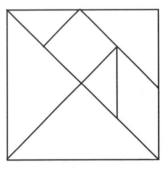

> **'Can you make one of these?' I said, picking up one of the pieces.**

> **'A parallelogram,' said John, and he attempted to make one from all the pieces.**
> **'Can you make one the same size?'**
> **John thought not, but Stephen put the two triangles together.**

They recognised that it was the wrong way round. Could they make it the right way?

'No,' said Stephen.

'Yes,' said John. He rotated the triangles together through 180 degrees, but it still wasn't right. He fiddled with the triangles, and at last he was satisfied.

'Can you make a bigger parallelogram?'

John put a square between the two triangles.

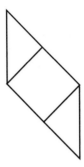

'Can you make it bigger still?'

This didn't take too long.

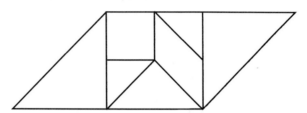

I left them with the problem of how many different parallelograms they could make altogether, but they had had enough interruption, and as I walked away they returned to the workcard, which asked for

'(i)   a rectangle

(ii)   a trapezium

(iii)   a parallelogram

from all seven pieces'.

From D S Fielker 'Some first year workcards', in *Mathematics Teaching*, No 66, 1974

CHAPTER 3

ANOTHER APPROACH

> … and in this chapter we suggest an alternative way of working. We consider the importance of discussion, view a sequence of lessons and comments on it, and see what the implications are for a teacher who wants to begin to adopt a new approach to the teaching of mathematics.

DISCUSSION

When my department started a workcard scheme for 11-year-olds, who were in mixed-ability classes, the teachers wrote their own cards and encouraged the children to work in pairs, as John and Stephen were doing.

There were early complaints from the teachers that not enough discussion was going on. I was looking at what was happening in one class when I first heard this, and I said, 'Look! Everyone is either talking to or listening to somebody!'

Ah, but it was not that sort of discussion they meant. What the teachers missed was the class discussion that they had hitherto been used to, where they knew all the time what was going on. Now there was a lot going on, they realised, but they did not know what it was.

Part of their concern was a genuine need to know. The teachers realised, I think, that part of their assessment of children, as well as their own teaching, involved a continual monitoring of the ideas which the children were expressing. There was also the realisation that marking a finished piece of work involved looking only at a sample of what had been going on, and that the teachers were used to listening to the whole process of problem-solving and investigation and the formation of ideas *as this process developed*.

Furthermore, a teacher can play a crucial part in a discussion, acting as a chairperson, relaying different opinions backwards and forwards, playing devil's advocate, intervening in subtle ways to ask a crucial question, introducing new ideas, influencing the direction, recalling earlier comments, comparing and contrasting, or perhaps importantly saying nothing at all! It was also these things that the teachers suddenly missed, because now they could only put themselves in this sort of situation with a couple of children at a time. And a couple of children did not produce the variety of ideas between them that a whole class did.

Let us see what can happen from a whole-class discussion.

A SEQUENCE OF LESSONS ...

My class of 10-year-olds needs to know something about prime numbers. However, prime numbers mean little on their own. They involve a knowledge of divisors or factors, which in turn involves a knowledge of multiplication facts, which we had been working on by looking at 100 squares (see page 76). Prime numbers are best seen in relation to numbers which are not prime, so they need to be put in a wider context, preferably in an interesting way.

I write on the board:

D1 = {1}
D2 = {

(I am using what is now an old-fashioned notation from the 'modern mathematics' of the 1960s, but it needs no explanation.) I wait – they are used to my waits! Someone suggests 'Two'. I accept this, but add a one also:

D2 = {1, 2}
D3 = {

I wait again. 'One, two, three.' I frown slightly, and write two of these numbers in:

D3 = {1, 3}
D4 = {

Now they are thinking. It is a guessing game, but guessing with clues, which keep changing. At each step they have formed a hypothesis, but each time the hypothesis turns out to be wrong, and they have to formulate a new one. 'One, four.' I can see what they are thinking, and it is perfectly justifiable, but it is not what I am thinking!

D4 = {1, 2, 4}
D5 = {

Now they are thinking again, hard! Another hypothesis is wanted. Some have an idea, but it has to be tested. 'One, five.' I accept that.

D5 = {1, 5}
D6 = {

Now they think they know. 'One, three, six.' I see what hypothesis has prompted this suggestion. Others say, 'One, two, three, six.' I will accept this, but not for a moment. Who agrees with the first suggestion, and who agrees with the second? Normally I would ask for reasons, but in this particular situation it is a pity to spoil the game by hearing them. What I can ask is who can see a good reason for either suggestion, and I am pleased that some can see a reason for both of them. But I accept the second one.

D6 = {1, 2, 3, 6}
D7 = {

Now it is becoming clearer, and as we progress to D15 everyone gradually joins in. Except the best mathematician in the class, who for some strange reason has to be told what the sets of numbers are! We explain it to him with some good-hearted amusement, and I ask everyone to write down the rest up to D20, just to make sure they all have the idea.

D7 = {1, 7}
D8 = {1, 2, 4, 8}
D9 = {1, 3, 9}
D10 = {1, 2, 5, 10}
D11 = {1, 11}
D12 = {1, 2, 3, 4, 6, 12}
D13 = {1, 13}
D14 = {1, 2, 7, 14}
D15 = {1, 3, 5, 15}
D16 = {1, 2, 4, 8, 16}
D17 = {1, 17}
D18 = {1, 2, 3, 6, 9, 18}
D19 = {1, 19}
D20 = {1, 2, 4, 5, 10, 20}

But this is only a preliminary. What do you notice?

- D stands for **divisor**, suggests one girl, and the rule is now explicit.
- All the sets contain 1. That's sensible, because 1 divides any number.
- All the sets contain the number itself: any number is divisible by itself.

- The set for 1 only has 1 in it.
- Some sets have just two divisors. These are all for odd numbers, except for D2. Well, says someone, this is because if a number is even it will have 2 as a divisor, so it will have at least three divisors: 1, 2 and the number itself.
- The numbers with just two divisors are the **prime** numbers.
- Is 1 a prime? There is some discussion on this. If a prime is a number with just two divisors, then 1 is *not* prime.

What are the next few prime numbers? Is 91 prime? What is the next prime after 100? And for homework, what is the next prime after 1,000? Yes, of course you may use calculators: what are you going to do with them?

We have not finished there. Next lesson, we look again at the numbers of divisors. Which is the first number to have three divisors? It is 4. Four divisors? 6.

Martin Gardner called 'abundant' those numbers which have more divisors than any lower numbers. So far we have 1, 2, 4, 6, 12. Can you find the next abundant number, the first to have more than six divisors? Can you find all the abundant numbers below 100?

We don't seem to have a number with seven divisors. Is there one? Which is the first?

Which numbers have an odd number of divisors? Why?

We had been doing work on angles, and talking about the Babylonians who are thought to have been the ones who decided that a complete turn should be divided into 360 degrees, either because of their experience in astronomy and a belief that a year had 360 days, or more likely because 360 was such a 'nice' number, and anyway they based their number system on 10 and 60. Is 360 an abundant number? How many divisors has it?

Back to primes. We colour them in on a grid in which all the numbers from 1 to 100 are arranged in rows of six.

1	**2**	**3**	4	**5**	6
7	8	9	10	**11**	12
13	14	15	16	**17**	18
19	20	21	22	**23**	24
25	26	27	28	**29**	30

...

Apart from the first row, the prime numbers (shown here in bold) all come in columns 1 and 5. Why?

We now colour in the primes on the 100 square (see page 76). There are four in the first row; four in the second row; only two in the third and the fourth; what *is* the pattern? There doesn't seem to be one. Will there ever be a row with one prime? With no primes? With more than four primes?

... AND SOME COMMENTS

There seemed to be a lot of ideas, all derived merely from looking at how many divisors different numbers had, and asking questions about that.

The general situation put prime numbers into a much more general context. Regarding a prime as a number with just two divisors is a much clearer definition than 'a number divisible by itself and 1'. The latter is more usual, but it is ambiguous about whether 1 is a prime. (It is not, as the children concluded.)

The wider context comes as a natural extension of this definition. If numbers with two divisors are primes, then it makes sense to look at numbers with other numbers of divisors. Square numbers have an odd number of divisors, and all numbers with an odd number of divisors are squares. Abundant numbers is a useful idea, and gives an excuse to look more closely at the divisors of larger numbers, and encourages a *feel* for the divisibility of some of them. The search for a number with seven divisors is made easier if we know we are looking for a square number. We could ask about cubes.

Although this is a summary of the sequence of lessons rather than a verbatim report, I have tried to indicate in a small space what sort of questions I asked and what sort of responses the children gave. Note how often the question 'Why?' followed a 'What?' – explanations were always wanted. Notice too how the initial guessing game was followed by 'What do you notice?' with some very worthwhile responses.

Finally, let us look specifically at how the work could be **differentiated** for children of varying ability in this very mixed class.

The initial game was something that everyone joined in, and everyone could have hypotheses about. The arithmetic involved is trivial for the low numbers with which we started, so it does not prevent even the worst calculators from having some ideas.

The question of the **next prime after 1000** produced a range of methods – and of answers! Everyone used a calculator, but the important thing is to know what to do with it (see the chapter Using calculators). Generally, the least able set out to divide each number in turn by several numbers to see if it had any divisors, but did not know where to stop, and they thought that 1,007 was prime because it did not divide by any number in their normal multiplication tables! When we discussed it afterwards there were ideas firstly about not dividing by 4, because it was not even, and not dividing by 9, because they had already tried 3. Gradually we worked towards the need only to divide by primes. The most able did not bother with the even numbers, or with 1,005, the obvious multiple of 5. Some of them recognised 1,002 as a multiple of 3 because it was 3 more than 999, therefore 1,011, 9 more, was also a multiple of 3. Those who carried on after the 12 times table found divisors for 1,007.

The **abundant numbers** required in principle a listing of divisors for all numbers up to 100. The less able did not get as far as that, but they worked out a lot of divisors in the process. The more able ignored the obvious non-runners and only checked the more likely candidates. It is not often that those who need more practice at arithmetic actually get it!

Not everyone found *all* the **divisors of 360**, which is quite a long list, but they did find most of them. It needed some sort of systematic approach to get things into order. The brighter ones were able to do some checking by pairing the divisors off as factors, and used strategies like converting 40×90 to 80×45. Those using a calculator may have saved themselves a knowledge of divisions, but they had to 'programme' their calculator in the sense of knowing what buttons to press and in what order.

The only person having trouble finding a number with **seven divisors** was a parent, whose daughter reported that he thought there wasn't one!

The **rows of six** were tackled surprisingly well by everybody. The sixth column has multiples of 6. The third column has the odd multiples of 3. (Multiples of 6 are even multiples of 3.) The second and fourth columns have even numbers, because they are 2 more or 4 more than a multiple of 6. That leaves only the first and fifth columns. These are 1 more or 1 less than a multiple of 6. (For the brighter ones, a prime above 3 is of the form $6n + 1$ or $6n - 1$.)

Colouring in the **primes on the 100 square** was straightforward, except for 91, which always causes a problem. We needed to programme a quick search through possible divisors in order to establish that it was not prime. What is not straightforward is the lack of pattern that occurs. This is an important property of prime numbers, that they do not have a pattern.

The question about more than four primes in a row was easy to answer. Primes above 2 have to be odd, but not multiples of 5.

The problem of a row without any primes at all is difficult, and no-one tackled it. No matter. If you pose questions with a wide range of ability in mind, then some of these questions may be beyond the ability range you actually have! One of the difficulties with textbooks is the tacit implication that at least the bright children should be able to answer everything. However, when you are in control, you or they can decide that something is too difficult and just leave it!

IMPLICATIONS

It would have been possible, after the sequence of lessons just described, to have the pupils return to a textbook and carry out some routine exercises on prime numbers and divisors. This would have been something of an anticlimax after the excitement and interest that had been generated, and in any case I was not using a textbook. However, let us look at the situation from the point of view of the primary teacher, who generally needs to rely on some form of scheme, but at the same time wants to provide a stimulating mathematical environment that suits the complete range of ability.

It is certainly feasible, at least on occasion, to conduct some sort of discussion lesson with the whole class.

The first consideration is merely one of **organisation**. Bearing in mind the possible structures outlined in the last chapter, it is difficult to conduct a class lesson when the class are all working on different topics, or are at different stages within the same topic. However, there are two possible opportunities:

1   If your pupils all work through a textbook more or less together, so that they all start a new topic at the same time, then you probably already begin that topic with a class lesson.
2   It is perfectly feasible to suspend the normal routine and have a 'one-off' lesson on something completely different.

The second consideration is **what you actually do** in such a lesson in order to provide for a range of ability.

It first needs pointing out very strongly that it is not necessary to conduct such a lesson in the way I have described. When I have given 'observation' lessons on teachers' courses, very much in this style, I have always pointed out that this is *my* style, and I never expect everyone watching to go away and copy it. If it makes you think about your own style of teaching in a critical and evaluative way, that is fine. You may feel happier about what you are already doing; you may wish to change some aspects of it; it is unlikely that you will want to change completely. Furthermore, any changes, if they do occur, will come gradually over a period of time.

In order to accommodate anything of the approach suggested here, it is probable that *some* changes will be necessary in what you normally do.

The whole point of such a discussion is that ideas come from the children, and not from you. You may find that you have to hold back from:

1   imposing your own ideas
2   making judgements too early about what the children say
3   ignoring or dismissing ideas that you think are incorrect
4   ignoring ideas that you think the rest of the class will find too difficult
5   asking leading questions
6   giving 'hints'!

This is not to say that it is always completely wrong to do all of the above things, but these are actions that I have observed in other teachers, when usually I would have avoided them!

If you are interested in the children having ideas, then you will need to foster these ideas.

That last sentence really needs rewriting in several different ways in order to emphasise each part of it.

You need to be *interested*. The interest is in what the children say, not in the immediate pursuance of the mathematical agenda that you have in mind. If the ideas of the children *are* your interest, then you will be less inclined to inject your own ideas. Fostering the children in their contributions means *accepting* their ideas, right or wrong. The class as a whole, in their arguments and counter-arguments, will sort out the good from the bad, the right from the wrong. Even if they occasionally come to a wrong conclusion, the important thing is that they be allowed to take part in the argument, the evaluation, the weighing up of reasons for and against given by their classmates. They will learn to listen to each other, instead of just to you. And they will also learn to make their own judgements, rather than relying on your authority.

(The point about ignoring the difficult idea is a rare one, but the situation does occur, especially if your class contains gifted children. I was presenting my oft-quoted calculator activity to a class of 8-year-olds, who were gradually finding that pressing 'x =' after a number multiplied that number by itself, and I had got as far as asking what I had to start with to press 'x =' and get 16. One boy said we had to find the square root. I asked him to explain to the others what a square root was. He said, 'It's like timesing by itself backwards!' *I* could not have given such an appropriate explanation!)

The third consideration is how you present the **mathematics**. That is what the rest of this book is about.

Section B begins by giving a number of different strategies for producing worthwhile mathematical activities that are suitable for a range of abilities, or starting points that can develop in a number of directions. Two of these strategies are then looked at in some specific cases in greater detail.

Section C looks at the main branches of the mathematics curriculum and selects some activities. There is full discussion of the mathematics involved, with particular reference to the more able pupils, but not forgetting the others.

It is important to remember that this is only a selection, and no attempt is being made to provide a full course which covers the whole primary curriculum in mathematics. It is the ideas, the strategies and the methods which are important.

SECTION

MAKING MATHEMATICS WORTHWHILE

This section is divided into three chapters:

4

STRATEGIES

This chapter makes some suggestions about what strategies you can use in order to turn routine problems, typical of those found in textbooks, into more worthwhile mathematical activities. None of the examples discussed are actually taken from textbooks, but some of them are typical of many such problems. I have used this strategies approach on teachers' courses, where I was able to use real examples from published schemes and invite the teachers to use the strategies in order to transform the problems into activities they could use back in their own classrooms.

COMPLETENESS: LET THEM FINISH

Here is a typical question:

This shape has a perimeter of 12 units:

Make three other different shapes which also have a perimeter of 12 units.

Why just three? Why not find *all* the possible shapes with a perimeter of 12 you can make on a geoboard?

This activity immediately involves something quite different from just more of the same work. Finding all the possibilities is a different matter from finding a given fixed number, or finding as many as you can, or even being told how many to look for and trying to find them all.

There are questions the children may ask. Is this board big enough for each of the shapes? Are we only looking for the shapes that do fit onto the board? How do you organise the search? How do you record the results? Is it necessary to record all the results? Are these two shapes the same, or different?

If we count them as different, what then? How do you know when you have all the possibilities? What do you do then?

Taking some of these questions, we can look at what the possible consequences are.

Note first that opening up the situation in this way does stimulate the **asking of questions**, and these should preferably come from the children rather than the teacher, and (it goes without saying) be answered by the children themselves. Asking questions is an important aspect of mathematical activity.

The most important thing is the **organisation** of the search. Finding merely 'another three' is a comparatively trivial exercise. The very fact that you want *all* of them means that you have to find a systematic method of going through the possibilities. This in turn means that there has to be some form of organisation, based perhaps on a combination of **classification** and **ordering**, that enables a count to take place.

Some of the shapes are rectangles.

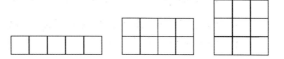

(Yes, a square is a rectangle, albeit a special one!) That does not get us very far. Maybe we notice that the number of squares is different for each one.

Are there other shapes made from five squares which have a perimeter of 12? These seem to work:

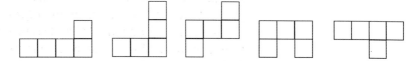

but this one does not:

Thinking about why that is so may indicate some ways of proceeding.

Alternatively, we can see that these shapes

all fit *inside* one of the rectangles shown above, and we can perhaps also see how each can be obtained with a sort of 'flip' of the corners of the rectangle, something that the rubber bands on a geoboard easily achieve, and we can see that this sort of transformation does not alter the perimeter. This is another useful way of producing more shapes with the same perimeter.

Whatever organisation is used, what happens is that the problem is broken down into a set of **sub-problems** that enables things more easily to be classified and put in order.

The organisation is of course more important than the result, and it is their organisation which will tell the children whether or not they have all the possibilities, rather than the answer in the teacher's book, or the teacher who will verify it for them. That is one reason why this book does not always give all the answers, and why it gives alternative methods. It is always tempting for teachers, with the best of intentions, to guide the children towards the organisation that they the teachers have in mind, with hints and suggestions and leading questions!

The question of whether and when to **record** is one that is too often precluded by the textbook telling you what to record, or the teacher providing in advance some paper printed with arrays of dots to match the pins on the geoboards. I prefer to wait, as the children pile different shapes on top of each other on the geoboard, or try to remember what they have constructed, so that they are obliged to *decide* that they need to record what they do as they go along; then I can give out some dotty paper.

It is worth considering what different pupils will get out of this sort of activity. **Differentiation** takes place because of the variety of abilities that is required. The brighter children will think of the methods of organisation, the sub-problems. The less able will be occupied with checking that the perimeter is always 12, a surprisingly non-trivial task here, and with thinking of shapes to draw. But all children will be working on sub-problems, and at their own levels reinforcing their ideas about perimeter, about shapes, about area, and about the general ideas involved in this type of investigation. In deciding what are duplicates they will be involved in seeing exactly what is the same and what is different about, say, these shapes,

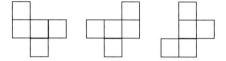

and perhaps working out the reflections and rotations that transform one into the other. (See the 'Four squares' activity on p. 108.)

Many children, incidentally, think that the diagonal of a square is the same length as its side, and will construct shapes like this one:

Some measurement may convince them otherwise. The brighter children may now like to take up this idea and see if they can construct such shapes which *do* have a perimeter of 12. Strictly speaking one cannot do this, but one can try to get close enough to 12 so as not to notice the difference, and the exercise is an interesting one anyway.

The diagonal of a square is approximately 1.4 times its side. In order to make up a whole number, we need five of these lengths to make approximately 7 units. This leaves 5 units to be made up from sides of squares. This is fine in theory, but try drawing it!

(A note is important here. Occasionally it is worthwhile asking *if* something is possible, even when you know it is not. One has to word the question carefully. Note that I wrote '… see if they can construct …' rather than 'Ask them to construct …'. So you would say to the pupils, 'Can you construct …' and not 'Construct …'. Mind you, you should also use this form of words when a construction *is* possible, otherwise the children will soon learn, as children do, that whenever you say 'Can you …', it will turn out to be impossible!)

Other sections in this book deal with things like finding all the pentominoes, or all the nets for a cube.

CONTEXT

Many mathematical ideas are treated in isolation, in a very limited way. The intention is presumably that they can be broadened later on 'when the children are ready'. Sometimes this may be the right thing to do. Addition of numbers is treated initially by counting groups of objects, and at that stage it makes no sense to put addition into a larger setting that would include addition of fractions or negative numbers.

However, there are times when a concept would benefit from a wider **context**, which is one consideration. Another consideration in *our* own present context is that the broader setting can also provide some interesting mathematics.

One example has already been given, the sequence of lessons on **prime numbers and divisors**. The argument is quite simple: prime numbers are those which have exactly two divisors. Now that we have focused attention on the number of divisors, we can look at *other* numbers of divisors. This, as we saw, led to several interesting ideas, investigations and problems that were suitable for children of varying abilities. Moreover, the activities enhanced and strengthened the concept of prime number.

Consider a geometrical example. The idea of a **diagonal** is a fairly simple one in the context of rectangles or squares, which is where it is usually met, and left!

One important discussion is about the difference in meaning which the word has within mathematics, on the one hand, and outside in 'everyday life' on the other hand. When I ask children what 'diagonal' means they will eventually tell me that it is a line which is 'not horizontal or vertical', which is a reasonable definition if we are considering everyday usage. However, in mathematics it means something more specific, and in fact is better viewed as a noun rather than as an adjective: *a* diagonal.

I can raise this issue by rotating the rectangle,

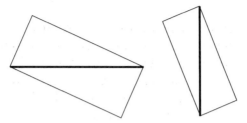

making the diagonal either horizontal or vertical! At this stage we need to work towards a **definition**. Definitions are never that easy for children, so we do need to work at it. I can begin by saying that diagonals are straight lines which join corner to corner. (The etymology is from the Greek: *dia*, through, and *gonia*, corner, so meaning a line going through the corners.) So how many diagonals has a rectangle?

Occasionally someone has said there are six! Now we can point out that four of them are sides, and these do not count as diagonals.

What about other quadrilaterals? We look at several we know, and they all seem to have two.

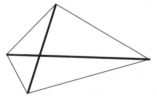

What about this one?

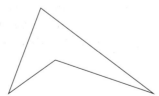

Now they are not so sure. Some think one. Some think two. Those who think just one are objecting to the lower diagonal because it is outside the quadrilateral. Well, who said it should be inside? Does it join a corner to a corner, without being a side? Yes, it does. So is it a quadrilateral? There are still some who say no! As I said, definitions are difficult for children: it has to *feel* right. It can be left for the moment: we have to work on those feelings.

How about a pentagon? We each draw one, draw in all the diagonals, and count them.

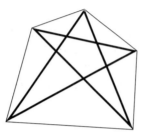

Does a pentagon *always* have five diagonals?

The children may need to draw some more. However, they can begin to see that since there are always five vertices or corners, the number of diagonals is not going to change. Unless, of course, the previous objectors to the diagonal outside the shape come up with this pentagon!

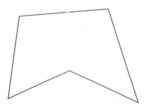

Now we can in fact use yet another strategy, which is to make use of the children's suggestions. We can keep the objectors happy by referring to these other diagonals as *external* diagonals, and we can ask what the possibilities are for pentagons with internal and external diagonals.

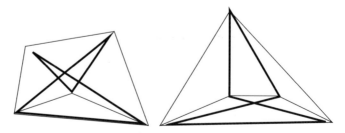

There is one further consideration here, which is that there can be diagonals which are partly internal and partly external

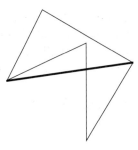

so we shall have to consider those as well. Using the strategy of *Completeness* we can now ask for *all* the possibilities for pentagons.

If the children can accept the idea of internal and external diagonals, then perhaps they can also accept this quadrilateral:

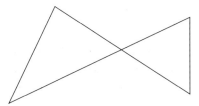

If so, it is interesting to see that both its diagonals are external. Now they may be able to find a pentagon which has all external diagonals!

Returning to convex polygons, where all diagonals are internal, we can increase the number of sides and see how many diagonals there are each time. (See the later strategy, 'Patterns and sequences'.) Basically it is a question of drawing and counting, but there are also some rules which emerge, and the possibility of a formula relating the number of diagonals with the number of sides, so again there is something there for everyone. (See the chapter 'Algebraic ideas'.)

We can widen the context still further. Where are the diagonals of a cube?

Perhaps the easiest to see are the diagonals of the faces:

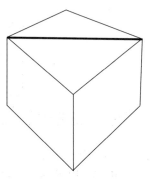

These, sensibly, are called **face diagonals**.

There are also diagonals that go *through* the cube:

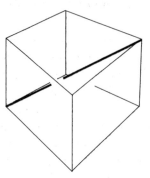

These are called **space diagonals**. How many of those are there?

There is obviously scope for some adroit mental work, some model-making, and further exploration of face and space diagonals in other three-dimensional shapes.

BACK TO FRONT

One nice thing about the perimeter problem with which we started this chapter was that instead of giving a shape and asking for its perimeter, which is always a fairly trivial exercise, it gave a perimeter and asked for possible shapes.

One can also do this with area.

How many shapes can you find with an area of 4?

Well, it depends. If you are working on a geoboard, then this limits the number of possibilities, and this becomes a 'completeness' question. Children will perhaps begin with the shapes made from whole squares (in a similar way to that indicated in the 'Four squares' activity in the 'Creating shapes' chapter), and as indicated there it is not a trivial task to justify how many of these there are.

They may think of half-squares:

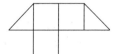 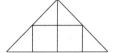 

At this stage the problem may start to look like an enormous one! 'There will be loads of them,' is a typical response. You can then ask them what they can do to make the problem more manageable.

They can decide to look at some sub-problems. What happens if they just look at shapes made from half-squares? Or find all possible triangles? Or parallelograms? Or restrict their shapes to those made on a 9-pin geoboard?

Whatever happens, note that a textbook exercise which consists of several similar questions about finding the areas of different given shapes makes far fewer demands than this one simple question. Here, as well as having virtually to find the area of each shape you make in order to justify that it is 4, you have among other things to think of what shapes to make, construct them, vary them, look at relations between them, classify them, order them.

The less able may find they have enough to do in adding half-squares together as they develop their feeling for area. The more able will be looking for other shapes, creating more of their own sub-problems, and perhaps finding some rules for areas of triangles or of parallelograms.

In effect this exercise presents the answer – the area is 4 – and asks what the question is. I have often put this more bluntly in a numerical context, and said to the children:

The answer is 10; what is the question?

An initial response (after a pause while they consider this unusual demand) is usually 5 + 5. They then think they have finished, but if I am still apparently waiting for more, they gradually continue with other sums of two numbers. The adventurous begin to diverge. They may add more than two numbers, or offer subtractions, multiplications or divisions. They may branch out from whole numbers and offer fractions or decimals. They may combine different operations. Patterns and sequences appear.

The first time I tried this with a class of 9-year-olds we covered two large boards with their suggestions, and we discussed all these ideas as well as some sequences which 'went on for ever'. The teacher thanked me, and said she had enough work for another three weeks!

Other examples in which the 'answer' is given and the 'questions' are asked for will be easy to find.

The answer is ½.
The area is the same as the perimeter.
The coins in my pocket add up to 73p.
I have stamps with denominations 1p, 20p and 26p; I have to stamp a parcel which costs £2.55.
The probability is 1 in 3.
A solid shape has 12 faces.
Straight lines are drawn from one side of a rectangle to the opposite side so that they produce 6 regions.

A different sort of reversal can be employed in other contexts, merely by changing over what is usually presented and what is asked.

In the discussion of diagonals above, we began by presenting, say, the quadrilaterals and asking where the diagonals are. Suppose we do this the other way round?

Here are the two diagonals:

Where are the sides?

What if the diagonals are here?

Now the focus of attention is definitely on the diagonals and their relative positions and lengths. In fact, noting the strategy of *Completeness* discussed above, we can investigate all possible pairs of diagonals, using whatever criteria we think suitable: they can intersect or not; they can be the same length or different; they can intersect at right angles; they can intersect at one or at both mid-points

We can extend this idea to other aspects of quadrilaterals.

Here are the vertices.

• •

•

•

How many different quadrilaterals can you draw?

What if the vertices are arranged like this?

•

• •

•

PATTERNS AND SEQUENCES

Another typical textbook problem is:

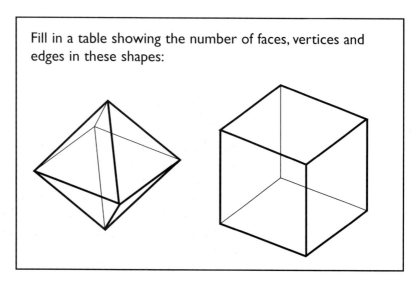

Fill in a table showing the number of faces, vertices and edges in these shapes:

Often a few more shapes are given, but they are usually a fairly arbitrary collection, and the object of the exercise appears to be to discover a theorem that gives a relationship between faces, vertices and edges.

This is fine, but we can do more than this by giving the situation a different sort of structure.

Consider this set of **pyramids** in which the number of sides (round the base) continues to increase.

SIDES	FACES	VERTICES	EDGES
3	4	4	6
4	5	5	8
5	6	6	10
6	7	7	12

Now it is fairly easy to see what is happening. The number of faces and the number of vertices increases by 1 each time, and is always 1 more than the number of sides. The number of edges is always twice the number of sides.

> What happens with a 20-sided pyramid? 100 sides?
> With *n* sides?

(See the 'Algebraic ideas' chapter for a discussion of how a general formula can be approached.)

Other sequences of shapes suitable for similar treatment are **prisms,**

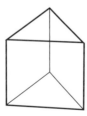 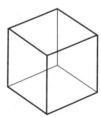 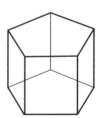

dipyramids,

and **antiprisms,**

The 'Algebraic ideas' chapter gives many other geometrical situations which can be developed in this way, and the 'Numbers' chapter gives some further ideas.

There are some problems concerned with which coins one can use to pay certain amounts of money.

Suppose you are confronted with a slot machine which only takes 5p and 10p coins. How can you pay for different amounts?

5:	5	1 way
10:	10, 5 + 5	2 ways
15:	10 + 5, 5 + 5 + 5	2 ways
20:	10 + 10, 10 + 5 + 5, 5 + 5 + 5 + 5	3 ways
25:	10 + 10 + 5, 10 + 5 + 5 + 5, 5 + 5 + 5 + 5 + 5	3 ways

How does the sequence continue? Why?

Now suppose that the machine recognises the *order* in which you insert the coins, so that 5 + 10 is different from 10 + 5.

5:	5	1 way
10:	10, 5 + 5	2 ways
15:	10 + 5, 5 + 10, 5 + 5 + 5	3 ways
20:	10 + 10, 10 + 5 + 5, 5 + 10 + 5, 5 + 5 + 10, 5 + 5 + 5 + 5	5 ways

How does this sequence continue?

BE VAGUE: LEAVE ROOM FOR INTERPRETATION

Most textbook problems are very clear about the conditions of the problem. If the problem is about pentominoes, pupils are told that the five squares *must be joined edge to edge.* Such precision may be necessary to delineate that particular problem. However, look what happens when the question is a little more vague.

> How many different shapes can you make from five squares?

As indicated in 'Four squares' in the chapter 'Creating shapes', some children are very imaginative about how they interpret 'made from five squares'. They join them at the corners, halfway along the edges, or with a mixture of these, and they use half-squares or other fractions of squares. Well, it is not absolutely essential that we work on just pentominoes today, and it is possible to consider what other problems have been thrown up by the children.

> How many possible ways can five squares be joined at their corners?

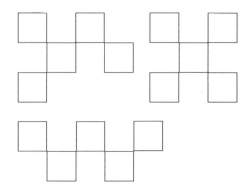

> How many possible ways can five squares be joined halfway along their edges?
>
> How many shapes can be made from joining ten half-squares?

The word 'different' is also open to interpretation. Are these two shapes different?

The textbook will categorically say no. The teacher may be tempted to do so also. But look at what sort of interesting problems are created by assuming that, when drawn on squared paper where the orientation appears to matter, these two shapes are different.

How many different orientations of this shape can we make? Which are rotations and which are reflections? What other pentominoes have the same number of orientations? What about this one?

Or this one?

What decides the number of different rotations and reflections that are possible?

I once asked a class how many numbers there were from 1 to 10. The straightforward answer, 'Ten,' was just a prelude to something else I had in mind, but the class had other ideas. 'Twenty,' said one; 'no – nineteen.'
'In that case it could be … not forty but … thirty-nine.'
'Or … seventy-nine.'

We embarked on this sequence, derived from thinking about halves, quarters, eighths, and so on. Then someone thought of decimals, and we had another sequence: 99, 999, 9,999, … .

Then I asked how many possibilities there were on a calculator that showed seven digits after the decimal point.

CHANGE SOMETHING

A problem can usually be turned into several new problems if some of its features are changed.

In principle, anything that is done with squares can also be done with triangles. So an investigation of **polyominoes** can be turned into an investigation of **polyamonds** or other shapes.

> How many different shapes can you make by joining together 5 (or some other number of) equilateral triangles? Or regular hexagons? Or 2-by-1 rectangles?

Some of the hexominoes are nets for a cube.

> Which pentominoes are nets for an open cube? How many different nets are there for a tetrahedron? An octahedron? A 1-by-2-by-2 cuboid?

Anything in two dimensions may have a corresponding problem in *three dimensions.*

> How many different shapes can you make by joining together 5 cubes?

The numbers on **dominoes** normally go up to a double-6, and a standard problem is to ask how many dominoes are in such a set.

> Suppose we only go up to double-5? Or we increase to double-7? What is the general rule?

Design *triangular* dominoes with three numbers on each, invent a similar game with them, and decide how many there should be for sets of different sizes.

What about *hexagonal* dominoes?

Dice have six faces, and there is a special way of numbering them, because the sum of opposite faces is always 7. How many different ways are there of doing this?

Design 'dice' with other than six faces, choose appropriate shapes so that the 'dice' are fair, and discuss how to number them.

If you cut a rectangle along its diagonal

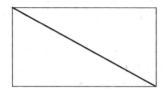

you produce two triangles that can then be joined together edge to equal edge to make how many different other shapes?

What happens if you do the same thing with a square? A rhombus? A parallelogram? A kite? What happens if you cut somewhere else?

If you add a 2-digit number to its reverse

$$
\begin{array}{r} 34 \\ + 43 \\ \hline 77 \end{array}
\qquad
\begin{array}{r} 56 \\ + 65 \\ \hline 121 \end{array}
$$

you always get a multiple of 11. Why?

What happens if you do the same thing with 3-digit numbers? 4-digit numbers? 1-digit numbers?

What happens if you find the *difference* between a 2-digit number and its reverse? What about other numbers of digits?

One of the suggestions in the 'Back to front' section above was to look at the vertices of quadrilaterals and construct the quadrilaterals from these. Why stick to quadrilaterals? Triangles

at triangles: the pupils need to discover that it *is* simple.
Pentagons, however, would be much more interesting.

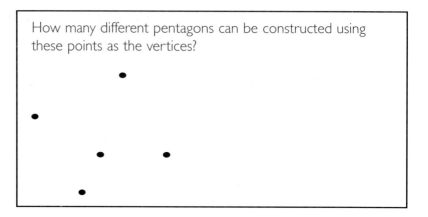

How many different pentagons can be constructed using these points as the vertices?

DON'T TELL THEM THE RULE

Many texts used to give instructions for making a shape such as a cube, instead of leaving it to the children to find out what the possibilities are.

 If the cube actually has to be glued together, then instructions for attaching some flaps are often given in the form of a diagram

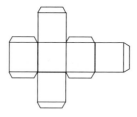

or a rule is given like: 'Put flaps on alternate edges'.

 It is much more interesting and profitable to ask the children:

What possible ways are there of arranging the flaps?

This involves some mental work in deciding which pairs of edges are going to come together so that a flap for one of them is needed.

 If we use the strategy of *Completeness*, then we shall also ask them:

How many different ways can the flaps be arranged for any given net? Is it the same number for all nets?

In general there are still too many texts that give a net for a shape, and all the children have to do is to copy it, cut it out and fold it up to make the shape. It is much better to present them with the shape, or a drawing of it, and ask them to design their own nets. Most shapes with flat sides become fairly easy with practice. A cylinder may present more of a challenge, especially if the required dimensions are given. So will a cone!

HERE'S THE RULE: WHY DOES IT WORK?

I once watched Jan Potworowski, in a beautiful parody of old-fashioned instruction, give an explanation for a method of subtraction, of which the following summary is a very inadequate description.

$$\begin{array}{r} 523 \\ -\ 274 \\ \hline \end{array}$$

'The trouble about this is that we have difficulty in borrowing and paying back, so a way of avoiding this is always to subtract from 999.'

$$\begin{array}{r} 999 \\ -\ 274 \\ \hline 725 \end{array}$$

'Now we have to add in the 523.'

$$\begin{array}{r} 725 \\ +\ 523 \\ \hline 1248 \end{array}$$

'This is obviously much too big. So we take the 1 from the end, and add it to the beginning.'

$$\begin{array}{r} 248 \\ +\quad 1 \\ \hline 249 \end{array}$$

We would certainly not teach this method in this way, and in these days of flexibility over algorithms we may not teach it at all, yet it would be difficult for children to think of it themselves. However, what we can do is present them with the algorithm (in the same way if we wish!) and ask them *why it works*.

A similar thing could be done with the flaps on the net of a cube, though this would come more naturally after the children had actually noticed that one of the ways of attaching the flaps was to attach them to alternate edges.

Is this a general rule?
Does it always work for any cube net?

If we also use the strategy of *Change something*, then we can ask if the rule works for a net of any other shape. This of course presupposes that the net for any shape has an even number of sides. It does, in fact. Why is this?

We can treat other algorithms for calculation similarly. If yours is a school in which children are always encouraged to invent their own algorithms, then any standard algorithm can be presented in this way and an explanation asked for.

If your children know the decomposition method of subtraction, you can show them the equal additions method and ask why it works. Or vice versa.

Here is the so-called *gelosia* method of multiplication, used by Italians in the 14th century:

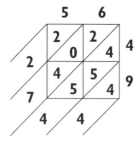

How does this work?

Occasionally rules are remembered or conjectured by children.
Ask for explanations for the following rules, and ask whether they always work.

To multiply by 10, you add a nought.
An even number ends in an even digit.
If the sum of its digits is a multiple of 9, then so is the number.
If you multiply a number by something, it gets bigger.
If you divide by a number by something, it gets smaller.
A square number never ends with a 7.
The angles of a triangle add up to 180 degrees.
When finding factors of a number, you only have to test as far as the square root of that number.
Apart from 5 itself, no prime number ends in a 5.

EXTENSION

Many of the above 'rules' can be extended:

There are rules similar to 'adding a zero' in order to multiply whole numbers by any power of 10: by 100, 1,000 etc. How does one divide by 10?

The test of divisibility for 9 by adding digits (see the third statement in the last list of rules) also works for 3, 27 and any other power of 3.

Square numbers do not end in 2, 3 or 8 either. (What about triangular numbers, or powers of 2, or multiples of 7, or … ?)

What is the angle sum of other polygons?

Apart from 2, prime numbers do not end in even digits.

CHAPTER 5

PEGBOARD GAMES

> Games are here used to do two things. The main purpose is the development of logical thinking in relation to the strategies that are used in playing a game. These particular games also develop other mathematical ideas, in terms of both processes and content.
>
> In particular these games illustrate the strategy of *Change something* described in the last chapter. We introduce a particular technique for effecting changes.
>
> Pegboard games are selected because they provide a nice variety which can easily be adapted for different numbers of players, and the materials are cheap and easily obtainable.

PEGBOARDS AND PEGS

Cheap plastic pegs, and pegboards with an array of 10-by-10 holes, are available from educational suppliers. Alternatively, pegboards can easily be home-made by cutting up appropriate pieces of perforated hardboard. These can be battened by cutting out mitred strips of timber and gluing them round the edges so that the board stands slightly above the table, enabling pegs to be inserted. An equally effective, if less elegant, method is to insert pegs *under* the board at the corners.

It is also possible to carry out the same activities using coloured counters on sheets of squared paper.

WHAT IS A GAME?

I define a game as an activity in which opposing players compete; this defines a goal, and can encourage thought about strategies. (There are times when children co-operate in order to attain a common goal; this type of activity is also worthwhile, but quite simply I do not call it a game.)

Some games are purely games of **chance**. A simple game in which two players throw a die, and the higher score wins, relies solely on the landing of the die and neither player has any control over that. There are some probabilities involved, but these enable the players only to assess their chances of winning at any stage, rather than actually to win. (If your opponent throws a 4, you know your chances of winning are 2 in 6, but there is nothing you can do to influence the result, except stop playing!)

Better games, from a learning point of view, are those in which some choice is available. As soon as a player has a choice, they have to determine which course of action is best, so **strategy** then comes into play.

Some games are a mixture of chance and choice. Ludo, for instance, is largely a matter of chance, but there is often some choice about which of your counters you should move.

FOUR-IN-A-ROW

Each player chooses a colour, and they take it in turn to insert a peg. The first player to obtain a row of four pegs in their own colour wins.

I usually demonstrate this game by playing a couple of rounds with one of the pupils. If there is not enough room for everyone to stand round and watch, then the demonstration can take place by using coloured chalks on a squared blackboard, or felt pens on a large sheet of squared paper. The pupils then play in pairs. I can make up a pair myself if there is an odd number of pupils, but I find it is better if I am free to wander round and observe the play.

One of the discussion points will be about what constitutes a 'row'. Everyone accepts rows that are parallel to the sides of the board

What about rows that are parallel to a *diagonal* of the board?

Usually that too is accepted, and with these possibilities there is scope for ample tactical play and subsequent discussion. Other variations will be discussed later.

After everyone has played a few games (they do not usually take very long), a discussion of tactics is appropriate. The first player in fact should always win, and if they do not, then it is because an error has been made.

In order to get four in a row you must first get three in a row.

```
○ ○ ○ ○
○ ◉ ◉ ◉
○ ○ ○ ○
○ ○ ○ ○
```

Now your opponent cannot stop you, because if they go at one end you can complete your row of four by going at the other end.

One object, therefore, is to stop your opponent from getting *three* in a row, unguarded by your peg at either end. This means that if they get two in a row,

```
○ ○ ○ ○
○ ◉ ◉ ○
○ ○ ○ ○
○ ○ ○ ○
```

you now have to put a peg at one end to prevent them from establishing an unguarded row of three.

One way to win, therefore, is to set up a sort of 'fork'

```
◉ ◉
◉ ○
```

which threatens a row of three in two different directions.

These tactics usually come out of a first discussion, and there are occasionally more subtle ones. The pupils can now play again to try them out. I explain to them that the object is to sort out a strategy for winning, not just to win, so that if they see an opponent making a mistake they should point it out and discuss it. I can encourage this idea by first playing another game or two with a pupil and demonstrating the co-operation that is possible, but it is not always easy to get the pupils to do this when they are concentrating on winning!

The sensible outcome so far is that it is interesting to go through all this play and discussion, but in fact if the first player always wins then it is no longer a good game – that is, it is not a *fair* game.

How can we make it fairer?

The pupils will have various suggestions. Two that frequently arise
are:

1   try to get *five* in a row;
2   play the game with *three* players.

These, and others, can now be tried out, though it may make
subsequent discussion easier if the changes are limited, and
furthermore limited to one at a time so that the effects of each in
turn can be determined.

What is a row?

Some pupils often think of other rules for what constitutes four
in a row. One favourite is a row with gaps.

○ ∘ ○ ∘ ○ ∘ ○

Here there is usually a feeling that the gaps should all be the
same, so that this arrangement would not be allowed:

○ ∘ ∘ ○ ∘ ○ ∘ ∘ ○

   Another frequent suggestion, that will often be tried out in the
course of play by an enterprising player, is a row at an oblique
angle to the sides of the board.

∘ ∘ ∘ ∘ ∘ ○
∘ ∘ ∘ ○ ∘ ∘
∘ ∘ ○ ∘ ∘ ∘
○ ∘ ∘ ∘ ∘ ∘

This can be more complicated, and in some cases, particularly
when there are other pegs around that prevent easy observation of
the row, some verification will be necessary. Pupils often like to
turn the board round so that they can 'see' the row from the end,
but in order to convince the other players, a better system is to
look at the 'steps' from one peg to the next. In the above example
each step is '2 along and 1 up'. (This is equivalent to the
description of the gradient of the line as '1 in 2', and will be an
important idea later in trigonometry and in co-ordinate geometry.)
   These reformulations of what a row is will have to be tested in
play.

Changing the rules

You can now ask the pupils how they could make the game more interesting, or more difficult, or just different. What can they change?

They already became used to the idea of changing the rules when they observed that the two-player game is not a fair one, and were able to pick on two things that could be changed: the number of players and the number of pegs in the target row.

They may also appreciate the idea that, in order to assess the effect of such changes, it is sensible to make one change at a time. If they suddenly jump to three players and five-in-a-row at the same time, they will not know the effects of each on its own. This is a sound scientific principle to do with design of experiments, and can also be applied to situations in mathematics.

In any case, children play their own games with each other outside the classroom and adapt the rules to suit local conditions. If there are far fewer than 22 players they still play football in the playground, perhaps with only one goal and a common goalkeeper! Cricket can be played with everyone fielding and taking turns to bat from the same end.

So, children are used to changing rules when playing their own games. They can do it just as easily in the context of a classroom game with some strong mathematical ingredients.

We shall discuss a little later how we can encourage them to do this in mathematics itself!

'What if not?'

A more sophisticated strategy for changing rules was outlined by Stephen Brown and Marion Walter in their book *The Art of Problem Posing*, published by The Franklin Institute Press in 1983.

If we apply their strategy to the original four-in-a-row game, then we begin by writing down all its characteristics, no matter how obvious or trivial they may be. They are as follows, numbered for reference later.

1   You have to get four pegs ...
2   ... in a row ...
3   ... next to each other.
4   There are two players ...
5   ... who play against each other.
6   The board has 10 by 10 holes ...
7   ... arranged in squares ...
8   ... in two dimensions.
9   You insert one peg at a time ...

10 ... of your own colour ...

11 ... where you wish ...

12 ... and continue with another peg at each turn.

13 The pegs are not moved.

14 The winner is the first player to get a row of four.

This is possibly the more difficult part of the exercise, because it is not so easy to identify the obvious and the trivial!

Now comes the 'what if not?' strategy. We can go through each property on the list in turn, and examine what will happen if it does *not* hold.

We have already considered altering the conditions for numbers 1 and 4, by changing respectively the number of pegs required in a row and the number of players. The effects of these are to change the tactics which are employed.

1   If the goal is five pegs in a row, a row of three is no longer a threat, but an unguarded row of four is. So a row of three must be prevented from becoming an unguarded row of four. In fact this defensive game is much easier now, so much so that it is not easy for anyone to win!

4   If there are three players, then there is no threat from three pegs in a row, because the two other players can block both ends. This does of course need some co-operation between them!

What are the possible consequences of changing the other conditions?

2   What if the four pegs are not in a *row?* If they have to form a *square*, of any size, then this in fact becomes a fascinating game in which a large amount of geometry is needed. Squares are not only set up with sides parallel to the board, but a whole range of others is possible with sides at oblique angles. The pupils will have to do some intricate counting of spaces 'up' and 'along' in order to convince the other players that they are indeed squares. This example is '2 along and 4 up'.

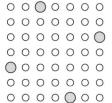

It is also possible to create some intricate 'forks' as in chess, like this one:

This threatens the completion of three squares. This is an excellent game for four or more players. The only practical difficulty in the classroom is that if there are more than two of them, some pupils forget whose turn it is!

3   If a row of four can have spaces in between, as discussed above, then this does not make a lot of difference to the advantage for the first player unless other conditions are changed at the same time.

5   There is a distinct educational advantage in playing two players against two, or in other-size teams, where instead of the players on each side taking turns, they consult with each other about the strategies. It is difficult in a classroom to do this without their opponents hearing, but if it is *supposed* to be done in the hearing of their opponents, then this is a good way of encouraging the general discussion suggested earlier.

6   The 10-by-10 board is adequate for most games, unless there are more than about four players. It is more interesting, however, to look at smaller boards, though this may mean the game is over before anyone has won. In this case some other conditions may have to be varied. If the board is 3 by 3 then the aim has to be three-in-a-row, and this becomes a very well known game!

7   It may be difficult to obtain perforated hardboard where the holes are in a triangular arrangement, or to drill your own. Use counters on a tessellation of regular hexagons.

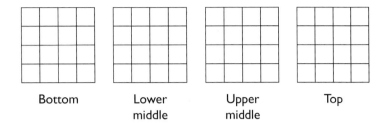

Bottom   Lower   Upper   Top
          middle   middle

8   A commercial game exists for playing four-in-a-row in three
     dimensions, in which rather than the first player who obtains
     a row winning, the winner is the player with the most rows of
     four. A two-dimensional representation can be used consisting
     of four arrays of 4-by-4 squares, one for each layer and
     counters can be placed in the squares. Now, as well as
     concentrating on the tactics of the game, players have to bear
     in mind the 'vertical' or oblique rows of four that can be
     constructed. Apart from the new strategies involved, this is a
     very good exercise in visualising the three dimensions from
     this two-dimensional representation.

9   An unusual variation is for each player to insert *two* pegs at
     each turn. However, in play this will be found to be too great
     an advantage for the first player, so perhaps the first turn
     could involve inserting just one peg.

10   Strange though it may seem, it can become a most interesting
     game when both players used the same colour!

11   There can be various restrictions on where you are allowed to
     place the pegs. You can try having to put them next to an
     existing peg, or *not* next to an existing peg. A sensible rule
     often used in the variation in which the goal is a square
     rather than a row, and in which multiple 'forks' can be set up,
     is to ban a move which creates a win. (This is provided that
     the other players notice it!)

12 & 13 Try restricting the number of pegs each player can use.
     When they have all been inserted, a move consists of moving
     one of the pegs, with perhaps restrictions about where it can go.

14   It is difficult to play so that the first person to make a row of
     four *loses*, but try it on a small board, perhaps with fewer pegs
     in the target row.

It can readily be seen that not only does a change of rules as outlined above produce many other different games, but in varying any combination of them, many more possibilities are created. I am by no means suggesting that they should all be explored! In any case, it is the pupils who should identify the variables and make the choices, and the list above describes some of the variations and their possible consequences, together with an indication of which ones could prove to be very interesting.

COST AND BENEFIT: WHERE IS THE MATHEMATICS?

One thing that may worry you as a teacher is the amount of time that this set of activities could take. You have a choice about this. You also have a choice about how it fits into your timetable: as a single block of time, a block of mathematics lessons, or an occasional lesson at less frequent intervals. And naturally you have a choice about stopping the activity if it appears to be using more time than is warranted for what your pupils are getting out of it.

All I can do, based on my own experience, is suggest what some children *have* got out of playing these games and variations.

First, there are some general benefits other than purely mathematical ones. Games are a useful means of learning, and not just about the subject matter involved. Children learn to work together. They learn to concentrate. They have to take note of what other players are doing and evaluate that, as well as think about their own plans. They have to co-operate with players in their own team. They have to co-operate with other opponents in preventing someone else from winning. They have to understand rules, perhaps interpret them, and keep to them, again in a co-operative way. They have to keep a long-term aim in mind and evolve a strategy, as well as concentrate on the minutiae of immediate play, the tactics. And as I have suggested above, a great deal of discussion can take place in which arguments about tactics have to be presented clearly, listened to, and evaluated. Generally, although players are playing *against* each other, co-operation is always required to play the game at all.

Some of the mathematical **content** involved in the original four-in-a-row game and its variations is fairly explicit. At a basic level, pupils have to count, and find and organise their way around a structured two-dimensional space. Otherwise, I can summarise some of the things that I said above. They need to be able to recognise a straight line, which in some of the variations is sufficiently complicated to warrant some discussion and some justification to other players, in terms perhaps of numerical ideas about gradient; and this has implications for the co-ordinate geometry of the straight line. When squares are being constructed, there is scope for a similar description of the way in which the sides of the squares slope, with implicit ideas about rotational symmetry that can be demonstrated by rotating the board through successive right angles. The three-dimensional version, if actually played in three dimensions, requires a familiarity with this microcosm of a three-dimensional space. If the pupils play this version on the two-dimensional paper representation, then it requires a complex understanding of the relationship which that representation has to the space it is representing, similar to that of other two-dimensional representations of three-dimensional structures, like plans and elevations, or perspective drawings.

There are also mathematical **processes** at work. These have to do with those aspects of mathematics that are not normally given in lists of contents or schemes of work. Winning a game involves solving a problem. Problem-solving is obviously mathematical if it is set in a mathematical context, that is, if it is a problem about mathematics. But the actual processes of problem-solving are themselves also mathematical, even if applied in some other context.

Problem-solving requires, among other things, a recognition of what the problem is; an awareness of what sub-problems may have to be solved on the way; the order – or orders – in which this may be done; strategies for doing all this; a recognition of whether strategies are working, and the adoption of new strategies if they are not; and the ability at any stage of the procedure to view the complete range of possible actions.

It is not difficult to relate these things to the basic game with which we started. Pupils must understand the object of the game; they have to build up their tactics; they need to make their moves in an appropriate order; they can tell if their tactics are working, and if not they can alter them in the next game; and at any stage they have to recognise and evaluate a number of different possible moves.

The game requires all these things, and one thing more. Every time an opponent makes a move, the situation may suddenly be changed and a fresh strategy may need to be evolved!

There is, after all that, one further process in which the pupils have been engaged: the identification of variables and the exploration of changing them, which is the 'what if not?' strategy. We can appreciate the full effect of this if we look at it in a mathematical context, which we shall do in the next chapter.

CHAPTER 6

NEW PROBLEMS FOR OLD

Here we develop the strategy of *'Change something'* by further examining the *'What if not?'* strategy discussed in the last chapter and applying it to the development of mathematical problems.

I had been working with a group of bright 10-year-olds with calculators. We had found that if you entered a number, then pressed '× =', the number was squared. This led us to an interesting exploration of squares and square roots.

Next time I was in the school, Tristan came up to me. 'Hey,' he said, 'you know that times-equals thing we were doing? Well, I wondered what divide-equals would do. So I put in 3, pressed divide-equals, and got 0.3333333.'

I spent the next two sessions with Tristan and his colleagues exploring this fascinating function, which at the time I did not know about!

PROBLEM POSING

The introduction to *The Art of Problem Posing* begins thus:

> **Why would you be interested in problem *posing* – an activity that has been neglected at all levels of education? A partial answer is that problem posing can help you gain deeper understanding of a standard topic and can enable you to see it in a new light. It also encourages you to create new ideas derived from any given topic.**

The idea of the authors is that students, of any age, can be involved in the 'What if not?' strategy in order to enhance their understanding of mathematics, and to create new problems. My own experience is certainly that pupils are able to create their own mathematical problems, given the right sort of open situations, and the opportunities to have this sort of independence.

The 'What if not?' strategy is a useful aid to problem-posing in a particularly structured way that can be taught, as the last chapter illustrates. I have seen Marion Walter, one of the above book's authors, work with teachers on this strategy, and it seems that whether or not it is passed on to the pupils, it is also a useful tool for the teacher in designing new problems or extending old ones.

I hope that it will be useful to both teachers and pupils. The above anecdote about Tristan shows that pupils can easily think in this sort of way. (It is taken a little further in the chapter 'Using calculators'.)

We shall look at a range of problems and show how, using the 'what if not?' strategy, they can be transformed into other problems, or used to put an idea into a wider context.

SUMS OF NUMBERS

$$1 + 2 = 3$$
$$2 + 3 = 5$$
$$3 + 4 = 7$$
$$4 + 5 = 9$$
$$\ldots$$

This is a very simple idea, that the sum of two consecutive numbers is always an odd number. Or, to put it the other way, any odd number (except 1, if we are thinking only of whole numbers and excluding zero) can be written as the sum of two consecutive numbers. One can ask why this is so, and develop some sort of **proof** (see the later 'Numbers' chapter). One can ask how to write, say, 53 as the sum of two consecutive numbers, and evolve an **algorithm** for doing this for any odd number. This is already a very nice and fruitful problem.

Let us list the characteristics:

1   Two numbers are added.
2   The two numbers differ by 1.

This appears to be all, so maybe there is not much that can be changed. However …

What if there are more than two numbers?

$$1 + 2 + 3 = 6$$
$$2 + 3 + 4 = 9$$
$$3 + 4 + 5 = 12$$
$$4 + 5 + 6 = 15$$
...

This begins to look interesting. The results can be recognised as multiples of 3. Why is this?

$$1 + 2 + 3 + 4 = 10$$
$$2 + 3 + 4 + 5 = 14$$
$$3 + 4 + 5 + 6 = 18$$
$$4 + 5 + 6 + 7 = 22$$
...

Is this what we expected? We might have expected multiples of 4, since sums of three numbers gave multiples of 3. On the other hand, sums of two numbers did not give multiples of 2.

How do we describe this set of numbers? Why do we not get multiples of 4?

$$1 + 2 + 3 + 4 + 5 = 15$$
$$2 + 3 + 4 + 5 + 6 = 20$$
$$3 + 4 + 5 + 6 + 7 = 25$$
$$4 + 5 + 6 + 7 + 8 = 30$$
...

Aha! Multiples of five! Why? Do we now know what will happen with sums of six consecutive numbers. Or with seven? Or with any number?

What if the numbers do not differ by 1?

$$1 + 3 = 4$$
$$2 + 4 = 6$$
$$3 + 5 = 8$$
$$4 + 6 = 10$$
...

We seem to get even numbers whether the two numbers we are adding are odd or even. Why?

$$1 + 3 + 5 = 9$$
$$2 + 4 + 6 = 12$$
$$3 + 5 + 7 = 15$$
$$4 + 6 + 8 = 18$$
...

These are multiples of 3 again. Why is this?

    1 + 3 + 5 + 7 = 16
    2 + 4 + 6 + 8 = 20
    3 + 5 + 7 + 9 = 24
    4 + 6 + 8 + 10 = 28
    ...

Now we *do* get multiples of 4. How come?

    1 + 4 = 5
    2 + 5 = 7
    3 + 6 = 9
    ...

    1 + 4 + 7 = 12
    2 + 5 + 8 = 15
    3 + 6 + 9 = 18
    ...

    1 + 4 + 7 + 10 = 22
    2 + 5 + 8 + 11 = 26
    3 + 6 + 9 + 12 = 30
    ...

Gradually, we can generalise more and more. It looks as though it is turning into a situation which is never-ending. But that means that if we can see why it is never-ending, and can establish what is happening, then we can cover all the rules by our ever-widening generalisations.

We can note two things:

1   After the initial stages, pupils will easily be able to generate their own further cases to investigate.
2   Everyone can do *something* on this wide problem. The less able pupils will be doing a large amount of simple arithmetic. As happened in some other situations, for a change those who need this sort of practice will probably get more of it than those who do not! They will also be learning or reinforcing ideas about odds and evens, and multiples of various numbers. More able pupils will be able to observe the patterns that are occurring and make generalisations. The most able will be able to explain these generalisations, and the generalisations of the generalisations!

This is the sort of situation where the 'What if not?' strategy turns a specific problem into a much wider one.

CIRCUMFERENCE AND DIAMETER

An early approach to the ratio of the circumference to the diameter of a circle can be a very practical one, which begins by measuring the distances round and across circular objects like tin cans and making some observations.

I prefer to avoid the traditional approach, which is then to ask the pupils to divide one by the other. Why should they do this? Only because the teacher is privy to some prior knowledge!

Given any set of such results, the pupils can be asked what they notice. It will be clear to at least some that one measurement is usually just over three times the other one. Then it is appropriate (preferably if the children suggest it) to do some divisions to see how true this is, and any anomalies can be explained as incorrect measurements which can then be checked. This is usually enough at primary level, and it is not appropriate to talk about π, or about the fact that it is an irrational number which when expressed as a decimal goes on for ever without any repetitions, and it is certainly not appropriate to give it to seven decimal places when the measurements made to find its value are themselves nowhere near as accurate as this.

So, we can stop there, and leave the rest to our secondary colleagues. Or, we can do a 'What if not' in order to put the idea into a wider context.

1   We used circles.
2   A circle is a regular shape.
3   We measured the distance all the way round, the perimeter.
4   We measured the distance across, the diameter.
5   We were concerned with two dimensions.

What if they were not circles?

Let us consider squares. What is the diameter of a square? If it is the widest distance across, it will be the length of the diagonal:

If it is the length of a line going through the centre, it will be anything between that and the length of the side:

The perimeter is 4 times the length of the side. If the square has a side of length 1, the perimeter will be 4, and the 'diameter' will be anything between 1 and (by measuring) about 1.4. So the ratio of perimeter to diameter will be between

$4 \div 1 = 4$

and

$4 \div 1.4 = 2.9$ approximately.

It may simplify matters, and as we shall see be more interesting, if we choose our diameter to be the maximum distance across the shape that goes through the centre.

If we take a larger square, say of side 2, then the perimeter is 8 and the diameter is about 2.8, so that the ratio is $8 \div 2.8 = 2.9$, as before. (This is not surprising because both measurements have doubled.)

We can now further investigate equilateral triangles, regular pentagons, regular hexagons etc. by using whatever plastic shapes are available and taking appropriate measurements.

Looking at even numbers of sides, where the diameter is the longest diagonal,

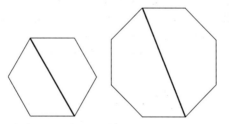

we can put the results in a table,

NO OF SIDES	4	6	8	10
RATIO	2.9	3	3.1	3.1

and see that the ratios seem to settle down to just over 3.

Regular polygons with larger numbers of sides can be constructed using a computer program like LOGO. It is not clear how to measure anything on the screen, and because of the degree of accuracy anyway, you will not get a closer ratio than 3.1.

However, on the screen it is possible to increase the number of sides sufficiently to make a regular polygon look indistinguishable from a circle, with the idea that we can get close to the ratio of circumference to diameter by considering a many-sided polygon, which in fact is the method Archimedes used to find a value for π.

What if the shape is not regular?

Let us look at rectangles.

A 1-by-2 rectangle

has a perimeter of 6 and a diagonal of length about 2.2. The ratio in this case will be

6 ÷ 2.2 = 2.7 approx.

For a 1-by-3 rectangle we have 8 ÷ 3.2 = 2.5.
For a 1-by-4 rectangle we have 10 ÷ 4.1 = 2.4.
For a 1-by-5 rectangle we have 12 ÷ 5.1 = 2.4.
For a 1-by-6 rectangle we have 14 ÷ 6.1 = 2.3.
…
For a 1-by-20 rectangle we have 42 ÷ 20 = 2.1.

It seems that the longer and thinner the rectangle becomes, the lower the ratio is. In fact, if we consider a *very* thin rectangle,

we can see that the diagonal will be practically the same length as the longer sides, and the ratio will be close to 2.

Brighter pupils will be able to see that this series of longer and longer rectangles produces a sequence of ratios which decreases towards 2, an example of a **limiting process** which they may meet later on when they are studying topics like calculus.

The shortest rectangle is the square, where the ratio was the largest: 2.9. So another important idea is that this ratio is the largest when the shape is **regular**.

Above all, we can see that the ratio is the same for all squares, or for all regular hexagons, or for all circles; in other words, for all shapes that are **similar**, in the sense of being enlargements of each other. Rectangles are not all similar, and this is why the ratio for them varies. This idea helps eventually to see why π, the ratio for a circle, is a constant, i.e. it does not vary.

These are fairly difficult ideas, and not everyone will appreciate the full consequences of them at this stage. But they will be able to involve themselves in finding or constructing the different shapes, making measurements as accurately as possible, calculating ratios (preferably using a calculator), and filling in tables.

THE ANGLE SUM OF A TRIANGLE

It is fairly easy to demonstrate that the angles of a triangle add up to 180 degrees. Note that measurement is *not* a good way to do this, since it can just as easily demonstrate that the sum is 179 degrees or 181 degrees! A favourite way is to cut a triangle from paper, tear off the three corners, and fit them together to make what is sometimes called a 'straight' angle

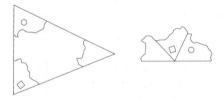

If each pupil has cut out a different triangle, this gives the *feeling* that this method will work for any triangle. A stronger demonstration is effected by marking out a large triangle on the floor and having pupils walk round it thus:

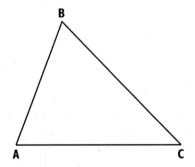

1   They begin by walking *backwards* from A to B.
2   At B, they turn to the left through the angle at B.
3   They walk *forwards* from B to C.
4   At C, they turn again to the left, through the angle at C. The angle is in fact behind them, so it helps if they have something pointing directly behind them as they turn.
5   They walk *backwards* to A.
6   They turn to the left through the angle at A.

They are now facing the *opposite* way from when they started, so they have turned, to the left, through 180 degrees. But altogether they have turned through each of the angles of the triangle, so the sum of them is 180 degrees.

It is clear (well, clearer than in the paper demonstration!) that this process will work for *any* triangle.

Some of the conditions of this theorem are:

1   The shape has three sides.
2   We add up the internal angles.
3   The shape is flat.
4   The sides are straight.

Now we can do a 'what if not?'

What if there are more than three sides?

We can investigate the angle sum of quadrilaterals. We know anyway that the angle sum of rectangles is 4 x 90 or 360 degrees. Is this also true for other quadrilaterals? The paper-cutting method still works, as does a variation of walking around a quadrilateral. Or, we can divide a quadrilateral into two triangles, and see that the angle sum of the quadrilateral is the same as the angle sums of the two triangles added together. (This method can also be used for polygons with a larger number of sides.)

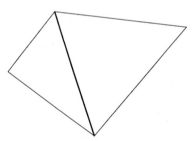

It would be interesting to look at quadrilaterals like this as well:

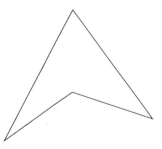

Pentagons are a little more complicated. We can get an idea by considering not a regular pentagon but this one:

Here the angles are right angles or 1½ right angles. Paper cutting produces an overlap, and walking around a pentagon needs a careful watch on how far you are turning.

A regular hexagon can be divided into six equilateral triangles, and that makes that particular one easy to see.

A regular octagon can be produced by cutting off the corners of a square, and that also gives an easy method.

An important idea is that the angle sum is constant for any polygon, and the walk-around method is most convincing. A general rule may be difficult to formulate at this stage, but there is a lot of profitable investigation here that can mostly be done in a very practical way, without actually measuring the angles, but with some nice bits of geometry.

We can add up the external angles

It depends what you mean by 'external' angle. The usual interpretation is this,

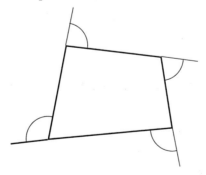

which leads to a nice result for which the walk-around method is very suitable. However, the pupils may have other interpretations of what an 'external' angle could be.

What if the shape is not flat?

Try drawing triangles on a sphere!

It needs a sphere on which you can draw shapes, and the angles may be difficult to measure. However, we can easily see, or imagine, one special case. A triangle is to be drawn so that one vertex is at the north pole, and the two sides from that go, respectively, down the zero meridian and the 90 degree west meridian as far as the equator. It is easy to see that each angle is a right angle, so the angle sum is 270 degrees!

Investigate further!

Given the right sort of construction material, one can make 'space' quadrilaterals. Or, imagine a quadrilateral which has vertices at the corners of a cube, like this

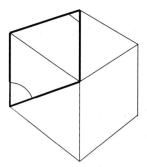

The two marked angles are each 45 degrees. The angle between the two sides drawn along the edges of the cube is 90 degrees. You may need the actual cube, rather than this drawing, to see that the fourth angle is also 90 degrees. So the angle sum of this 'space' quadrilateral is 270 degrees! What other possibilities are there?

What if the sides are curved?

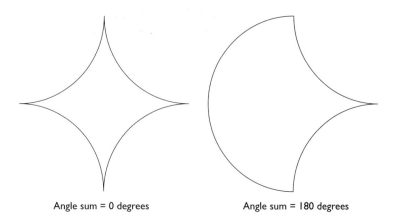

Angle sum = 0 degrees   Angle sum = 180 degrees

Get out the compasses and start experimenting!

SECTION C

SOME MATHEMATICAL TOPICS

This section is divided into seven chapters:

CHAPTER 7
Numbers

CHAPTER 8
Algebraic ideas

CHAPTER 9
Creating shapes

CHAPTER 10
Perimeter and area

CHAPTER 11
Using calculators

CHAPTER 12
Dice and probability

NUMBERS

This chapter deals essentially with some basic numerical ideas. Children already have some feeling for numbers and relationships between them, based on their experiences with computation. The activities which are outlined here put those ideas into new and challenging contexts, which focus sharper attention on the properties and relationships involved, and develop some new ideas. They can also bring forward ideas from their intuitive state to a more explicit awareness, leading to a more structured and formal description of them.

ODDS AND EVENS

Children are used to the ideas of odd and even numbers, so much so that it becomes second nature to recite 'Two, four, six, eight, …' or even 'One, three, five, seven, …', without considering what even or odd numbers really are, or what properties they have.

One way of reintroducing the idea is to show, say, a string of Unifix cubes arranged red, yellow, red, yellow,…

R	Y	R	Y	R	Y	R	Y	R	Y

and explain that they are numbered from left to right, so that 1 is red, 2 is yellow, and so on. What colour is 20? 91? 43? 1,001? 1 million? How do you know?

The children will know, for instance, that 91 is red because it is odd, but *how* do they know it is odd? Because it ends in an odd number, they usually say. (They mean odd **digit**, and one can clarify the difference between number and digit, and perhaps explain that outside the classroom many people confuse the two words!) But why do odd numbers end in odd digits, and even numbers in even digits? Again, the usual explanation offered is that when you start counting, the odds and evens come alternately, and the last digits also therefore alternate.

There are two problems here. One is the tendency of children to prefer to describe things *sequentially*, in the manner just described.

$$1 \to 2 \to 3 \to 4 \to \ldots \quad 2 \to 4 \to 6 \to 8 \to \ldots \quad 1 \to 3 \to 5 \to 7 \to \ldots$$

In the same way they will, for instance, say that 93 is a multiple of 3 because 90 is a multiple of 3, and 93 is *3* more than 90. This is perfectly acceptable, and as we shall see involves important ideas about numbers. However, we also want to encourage an alternative way of thinking about relationships between numbers. 90 is a multiple of 3 because it is 3 times something, i.e. 3 times 30. So we can say 93 is a multiple of 3 because it is 3 times 31. In the same way, even numbers are multiples of 2, so 94 is even because it is 2 times 47.

We can illustrate the two ways of thinking about these numbers with a diagram

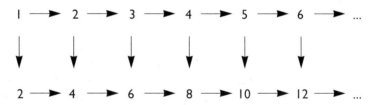

The arrows going to the right illustrate sequential thinking: add 1 to each natural number to get the next, or 2 to each even number to get the next. The arrows going down illustrate a different kind of relational thinking: take the natural number and double it to get the corresponding even number.

> It may indeed help to ask questions like 'What is the seventh even number?' or 'What is the tenth odd number?'
>
> It may also help to ask whether zero is odd or even.

However, some children have declared that zero is neither! And if it has to be one or the other, then they opt for even because it 'comes before an odd'! It can be more difficult to realise that it is even because $0 = 0 \times 2$.

The second problem about recognition of odds and evens is the over-familiarity with last digits, which militates against thinking about why they are so crucial. The simple answer is so elusive: without the units digit any number is so many *tens*, which is even. So the oddness or evenness depends entirely on the last digit.

This in turn depends on another simple idea, which most children seem to appreciate, that odd plus even is odd, and even plus even is even. This idea can be raised from the array of red and yellow cubes in the following way:

What happens when you add two red numbers?

This needs careful handling. If we take just one example, say 3 + 5 = 8, which is yellow, do we know that *all* cases are going to give us a yellow number? How many cases do we have to try before we are sure? The children should decide this, but usually they will explain that this is because 'two odds give an even'. A wise teacher will still ask why *this* is so. Explanations vary, but the essential thing is that an odd number is a multiple of 2 plus 1 more, so the sum of two odd numbers is two multiples of 2 plus *2* more; and this is also a multiple of *2*. A representation on squared paper or with cubes will help;

the two 'spare' cubes will join to make another pair.

What other combinations of colours can be added?

These can be pursued in the same way, except that the children should be asked to decide what the other combinations are, and whether red + yellow is the same as yellow + red.

Once the various combinations of odd and even have been established,

odd + odd = even
odd + even = odd
even + odd = odd
even + even = even

they can be summarised in the sort of addition table with which the children may already be familiar:

+	odd	even
odd	even	odd
even	odd	even

There is a remaining pedagogical problem, and that is that odds and evens *are* familiar to children, and that this familiarity can militate against analysis of them, as has been suggested. The activities described, however, help to put the familiar ideas into a *new context* that invites reconsideration of previously held ideas. Compare the *Context* strategy discussed in the 'Strategies' chapter earlier.

MULTIPLES OF THREE

The next array of Unifix cubes is arranged in the sequence red, yellow, blue, red, yellow, blue, …

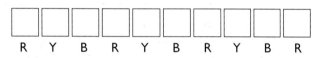

| R | Y | B | R | Y | B | R | Y | B | R |

and they are again numbered from the left in order. We can now ask similar questions.

What colour is 20? 30? 99? 1 million? What is the next blue number after 40? After 100? Etc.

What happens if you add two red numbers? Two blue numbers? A red and a yellow? Etc.

The children, incidentally, are never confused by the fact that the *new* red and yellow numbers are different from the old ones. But they often get hooked onto the odds and evens, and will tell you that 'the blue ones are either odd or even' without realising that this does not tell you anything about them!

As before, questions can be asked about combinations of colours, and the results can be summarised in a table:

+	R	Y	B
R	Y	B	R
Y	B	R	Y
B	R	Y	B

Apart from the change of colours, there is now an essential difference. In the previous situation, numbers were either yellow or red, even or not-even, and the not-even numbers were odd. Now, however, the blue numbers are multiples of 3, but the not-multiples of 3 are of two kinds, red and yellow. How can we distinguish between the two?

The situation may become clearer if we ask why, say, red plus red is yellow. Explanations usually run along the lines of: red is 1 more than a multiple of 3, so two reds will be 2 more than *two* multiples of 3, which is 2 more than a multiple of 3 (because two multiples of 3 added together give a multiple of 3), which is yellow.

Both situations, two colours and three colours, can provide the opportunity for some simple algebraic notation (see the 'Development and differentiation' section below).

It is also possible to investigate further sequences such as red, yellow, blue, green, … . However, essentially no new ideas are produced, and adding more colours does not really warrant the extra work involved.

INCLUSION AND INTERSECTION

1	2	3	4	5	6	7	8	9	10
11	12	13	14	15	16	17	18	19	20
21	22	23	24	25	26	27	28	29	30
31	32	33	34	35	36	37	38	39	40
41	42	43	44	45	46	47	48	49	50
51	52	53	54	55	56	57	58	59	60
61	62	63	64	65	66	67	68	69	70
71	72	73	74	75	76	77	78	79	80
81	82	83	84	85	86	87	88	89	90
91	92	93	94	95	96	97	98	99	100

Children will probably have used the 100 square to colour in sets of multiples, and will have noticed some of the patterns these make. If not, this can be an introductory activity. The patterns will range from the dullness of the multiples of 2, 5 and 10,

1	2	3	4	5	6	7	8	9	10
11	12	13	14	15	16	17	18	19	20
21	22	23	24	25	26	27	28	29	30
31	32	33	34	35	36	37	38	39	40
41	42	43	44	45	46	47	48	49	50
51	52	53	54	55	56	57	58	59	60
61	62	63	64	65	66	67	68	69	70
71	72	73	74	75	76	77	78	79	80
81	82	83	84	85	86	87	88	89	90
91	92	93	94	95	96	97	98	99	100

1	2	3	4	5	6	7	8	9	10
11	12	13	14	15	16	17	18	19	20
21	22	23	24	25	26	27	28	29	30
31	32	33	34	35	36	37	38	39	40
41	42	43	44	45	46	47	48	49	50
51	52	53	54	55	56	57	58	59	60
61	62	63	64	65	66	67	68	69	70
71	72	73	74	75	76	77	78	79	80
81	82	83	84	85	86	87	88	89	90
91	92	93	94	95	96	97	98	99	100

1	2	3	4	5	6	7	8	9	10
11	12	13	14	15	16	17	18	19	20
21	22	23	24	25	26	27	28	29	30
31	32	33	34	35	36	37	38	39	40
41	42	43	44	45	46	47	48	49	50
51	52	53	54	55	56	57	58	59	60
61	62	63	64	65	66	67	68	69	70
71	72	73	74	75	76	77	78	79	80
81	82	83	84	85	86	87	88	89	90
91	92	93	94	95	96	97	98	99	100

to the complexities of 4 and 7.

1	2	3	4	5	6	7	8	9	10
11	12	13	14	15	16	17	18	19	20
21	22	23	24	25	26	27	28	29	30
31	32	33	34	35	36	37	38	39	40
41	42	43	44	45	46	47	48	49	50
51	52	53	54	55	56	57	58	59	60
61	62	63	64	65	66	67	68	69	70
71	72	73	74	75	76	77	78	79	80
81	82	83	84	85	86	87	88	89	90
91	92	93	94	95	96	97	98	99	100

1	2	3	4	5	6	7	8	9	10
11	12	13	14	15	16	17	18	19	20
21	22	23	24	25	26	27	28	29	30
31	32	33	34	35	36	37	38	39	40
41	42	43	44	45	46	47	48	49	50
51	52	53	54	55	56	57	58	59	60
61	62	63	64	65	66	67	68	69	70
71	72	73	74	75	76	77	78	79	80
81	82	83	84	85	86	87	88	89	90
91	92	93	94	95	96	97	98	99	100

The pattern for 10 can easily be explained: the numbers are arranged in rows of 10, so the multiples of 10 come at the ends of the rows. Similarly, the multiples of 5 come halfway along the rows as well as at the ends.

An important idea is that *the multiples of 10 are included in the multiples of 5*. We need to discuss this in a more general context.

If a number is divisible by 10, why is it also divisible by 5?

Well, what is a multiple of 10? It is 10 times something. If it is 10 times something, why is it also 5 times something? Because 10 is 5 times 2! But that statement alone does not necessarily make the situation clear.

A practical approach will help. 30 cubes can be arranged as 3×10:

But each 10 can be seen as two 5s:

Hence, 30 is also 6 × 5. The pattern of the cubes, especially if several different examples are taken, embodies a generalisation. One can easily imagine doing this with *any* number of cubes.

We can see this pattern of

10 = 1 × 10 = 2 × 5
20 = 2 × 10 = 4 × 5
30 = 3 × 10 = 6 × 5

etc.

which also embodies another feature of products of two numbers, that if you multiply the first by 2 and divide the second by 2, the product is unchanged. This is a feature that children sometimes intuitively use in order to make calculation easier: 26 × 5 is the same as 13 × 10, which is easier to work out. This idea can also be demonstrated practically with the cubes: in the example just given, a rearrangement of the cubes will give a 6-by-5 array.

A more formal way of looking at the same idea is to note that

30 = 5 × 2 × 6

and this can be seen as

5 × (2 × 6)

or

(5 × 2) × 6.

A more general way of looking at this idea of inclusion is to put number tablets onto Venn diagrams. Choose the two sets to be multiples of 3 and multiples of 4.

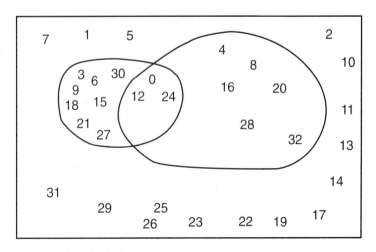

It becomes clear, as numbers are inserted, that the **intersection** – that is the region of overlap between the two sets – contains the numbers that are multiples of both 3 and 4, that is multiples of 12. Note that the numbers which are not multiples of 3 or 4 appear on the diagram, outside the two rings. Note also that it is useful to have a number tablet for zero, so that its placing can be discussed.

Children may think that the rule is to multiply the 3 and 4 to get 12. So ...

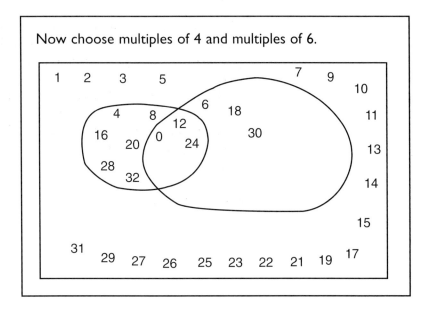

Now choose multiples of 4 and multiples of 6.

This time, the intersection still contains multiples of 12! Well, 12 in fact is the *lowest* number that 4 and 6 will divide into.

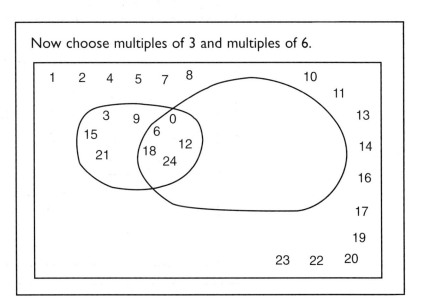

Now choose multiples of 3 and multiples of 6.

Some children think that the intersection is again going to be multiples of 12, but this time it is multiples of 6. This is because multiples of 6 are also multiples of 3 – the inclusion idea again. Why is one region empty? Because you cannot have multiples of 6 which are not multiples of 3.

A diagram for three sets will pose some more general problems: choose the sets to be multiples of 3, 4 and 5.

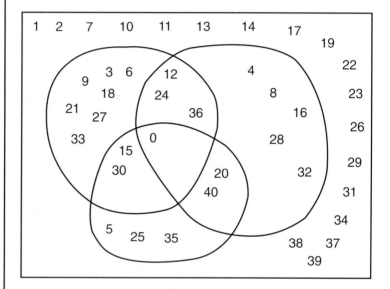

Explain which sets of numbers are in each of the eight regions.

We have already dealt with multiples of 3 and 4. Other pairs of multiples intersect in a similar way. But the intersection of all three sets of multiples of 3, 4 and 5 respectively contains multiples of 60.

Let the children choose their own three sets.

Now they are likely to choose three numbers which provide some interesting complications. Note what happens for multiples of 3, 4 and 6.

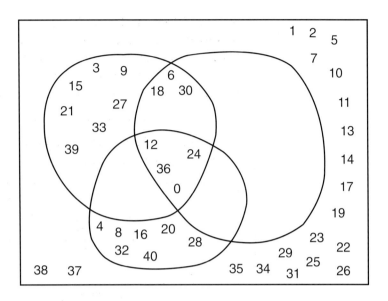

Patterns and place value

Let us return to the 100 square and look at the pattern for multiples of 4:

1	2	3	4	5	6	7	8	9	10
11	12	13	14	15	16	17	18	19	20
21	22	23	24	25	26	27	28	29	30
31	32	33	34	35	36	37	38	39	40
41	42	43	44	45	46	47	48	49	50
51	52	53	54	55	56	57	58	59	60
61	62	63	64	65	66	67	68	69	70
71	72	73	74	75	76	77	78	79	80
81	82	83	84	85	86	87	88	89	90
91	92	93	94	95	96	97	98	99	100

Why this pattern? Why no multiples of 4 in the odd columns? Why do they occur only in the even multiples of 10? If a number ends in a 4, why is the tens digit even? If a number ends in a 6, why is the tens digit odd?

Explanations are perhaps to do with the fact that 10 is two 4s and a 2, and two 10s will be five 4s, but the children will have various ideas.

They will notice the 'knight's moves', typified by the transformation from 4 to 16. How do we get there? A knight's move is 'two along and one to the side', in this case two to the right and one down. What is the effect of two to the right? It adds 2. And one down? It adds 10. The result is a total addition of 12. 12 is a multiple of 4. So if we start with a multiple of 4, and add 12, we get a multiple of 4.

Some arrows will help to create some diagrams

1	2	3	4	5	6	7	8	9	10
11	12	13	14	15	16	17	18	19	20
21	22	23	24	25	26	27	28	29	30
31	32	33	34	35	36	37	38	39	40
41	42	43	44	45	46	47	48	49	50
51	52	53	54	55	56	57	58	59	60
61	62	63	64	65	66	67	68	69	70
71	72	73	74	75	76	77	78	79	80

This way we can build up an idea of how to add **directed numbers**. Since adding 2 and then adding 10 is equivalent to adding 12, we can write this as

$$(+2) + (+10) = +12.$$

Similarly

$$(+2) + (-10) = -8$$

can be a way of recording 'adding 2 and subtracting 10 is equivalent to subtracting 8'. Each pair of arrows, it turns out, represents the addition or subtraction of a multiple of 4, which is why the knight's moves occur.

Even without the formality of the notation, children will see that moving downwards adds 10, moving upwards subtracts 10, moving to the right adds 1, and moving to the left subtracts 1, and they will therefore be able to combine these moves numerically.

This will also reinforce ideas about using place value to perform calculation mentally. To add 12, add 10 and then add 2 (or vice versa). To add 8, add 10 then subtract 2.

> Now the children can investigate the patterns made by other sets of multiples, and explain them in similar ways.

This will again lead to similar ideas about directed numbers and calculations. The multiples of 9 form a 'diagonal' line because adding 9 is equivalent to adding 10 and subtracting 1. Another 'diagonal' is produced from multiples of 11.

1	2	3	4	5	6	7	8	9	10
11	12	13	14	15	16	17	18	19	20
21	22	23	24	25	26	27	28	29	30
31	32	33	34	35	36	37	38	39	40
41	42	43	44	45	46	47	48	49	50

Multiples of 8 produce knight's moves because adding 8 is like adding 10 and subtracting 2. Multiples of 7 produce the pattern they do because adding 7 is like adding 10 and subtracting 3.

1	2	3	4	5	6	7	8	9	10
11	12	13	14	15	16	17	18	19	20
21	22	23	24	25	26	27	28	29	30
31	32	33	34	35	36	37	38	39	40
41	42	43	44	45	46	47	48	49	50

PUZZLES AND PROBLEMS

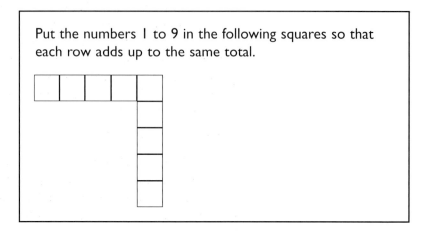

Put the numbers 1 to 9 in the following squares so that each row adds up to the same total.

It is best to use number tiles or at least pieces of paper with the numbers written on them. This gives more flexibility for movement and saves lots of erasing.

Trial and error is a first approach, and one where the children can practise much mental arithmetic. They soon find solutions, and there are many. However, because they often begin with the numbers in order, the 5 tends to stay in the corner.

1	9	3	7	5
				2
				4
				6
				8

The order of the rest of numbers in each row obviously does not matter, though this will need to be discussed with those children who think that rearranging the numbers within one row creates a different solution. So, if we keep the 5 in the corner, different solutions depend on interchanging the numbers *between* the two rows. Discussion reveals that this cannot be done by changing single numbers but only by changing at least *pairs* of numbers which add to the same, and there are several possibilities here.

What solutions are there with other numbers in the corner?

Children try different possibilities. It looks as if solutions can be found if an odd number is in the corner, but not if an even number is put there. Why is this?

Try 6 in the corner. What is left? That is, what is the total of the remaining numbers? This is 39. Can we split the 39 up equally between the two rows? No.

The explanation has something to do with the total of the numbers from 1 to 9:

$$1 + 2 + 3 + 4 + 5 + 6 + 7 + 8 + 9$$

It is worth asking what the best way is of adding them. Often a suggestion is to pair them from the outside in, to make tens: $1 + 9$, $2 + 8$, $3 + 7$, $4 + 6$, and a 5: four 10s and a 5, or 45. A slightly more sophisticated description would be four-and-a-half tens.

This method of addition is important, because it suggests a generalisation that can be applied to other similar sums. What is the sum of the numbers from 1 to 20? If we use the same method then the first and last add to 21, and so do all the other pairs as we work inwards

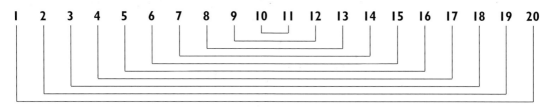

How many pairs? In this case ten of them, so the total is $10 \times 21 = 210$.

To return to the numbers 1 to 9, the total there was 45. Now the explanation can be given. The number in the corner is counted twice, so the apparent total of *all* the numbers is 45 plus the corner number. In order to be able to divide this total between the two rows, it must be even. If the corner number plus 45 is to be even then the corner number must be odd.

Now it is easy to put each of the odd numbers in turn in the corner and find a solution. For example, with 1 in the corner the total will be $45 + 1 = 46$, so each row will total 23. This leaves 22 for the other numbers on each row. Trial and error and mental arithmetic perhaps yields 2, 4, 7 and 9:

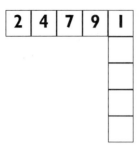

The rest of the numbers, 3, 5, 6 and 8, automatically sum to 22! This illustrates the power of working things out in theory first!

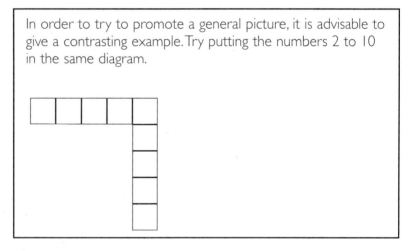

In order to try to promote a general picture, it is advisable to give a contrasting example. Try putting the numbers 2 to 10 in the same diagram.

This time it is necessary to sum the numbers from 2 to 10. We can do this in the same way, by adding them in pairs from the outside in, but children sometimes look at the change from the previous sum: 1 to 9 summed to 45; we have removed the 1 and added a 10, which is equivalent to adding 9 to the 45. (Note the similarity to the moves on the 100 square.) Alternatively, we can see that we have added 1 to each of the numbers from 1 to 9, so altogether we have added 9 to 45. It is always a good thing to do such a calculation in different ways: for one thing, it is a check on the correctness of the answer; for another, it is useful to share different ways of working. Whichever way, the sum is 54, which is even. So this time it is necessary to put an *even* number in the corner in order to keep the total even.

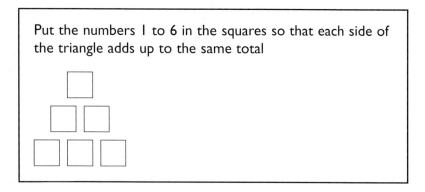

Put the numbers 1 to 6 in the squares so that each side of the triangle adds up to the same total

Again, trial and error will be a first approach, perhaps with an initial attempt such as this, where the sums of the sides are 6, 12 and 12.

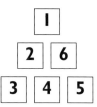

Various adjustments are now possible. A solution can quickly be reached by removing the numbers at the middle of the sides and putting them back, the largest between the 1 and 3, and so on. Or, since the total is 6 + 12 + 12 = 30, each side must sum to 10.

In order to find other solutions, the corner numbers are again crucial. The total of 1 to 6, 21, is already a multiple of 3, so the corner numbers must also add to a multiple of 3.

One useful sub-problem is to list all the possible ways in which this can happen. This exercise requires putting the triples in some sort of logical order so that none is left out. One possible ordering is:

1, 2, 3   1, 2, 6   1, 3, 5   2, 3, 4   3, 4, 5   4, 5, 6

However, only some of these will work out, and there are logical arguments for why the others will not do so.

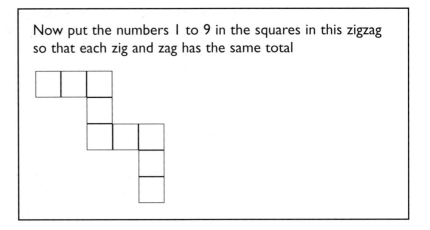

Now put the numbers 1 to 9 in the squares in this zigzag so that each zig and zag has the same total

Trial and error may still be a way to begin, but it is less likely that the children will find a solution this way. You will eventually need to relieve the frustration by discussing what goes in the corners, and what sort of number the augmented total has to be.

There are four zigs and zags, so the final total must be a multiple of 4. The numbers in the three corners are going to be counted twice, so their sum must be added to 45, to give a multiple of 4. What are the possibilities?

The multiples of 4 above 45 are

48, 52, 56, and so on,

so the sums to be added to 45 to get these are

3, 7, 11 and so on.

3 cannot be made from adding three corner numbers together because it is too small. 7 can only be made from $1 + 2 + 4$. The total will be $45 + 7 = 52$, so each row must add to a quarter of this, or 13. However, this needs careful thought. 1 and 2 cannot appear in the same row because there is not a 10 to put with them. So the 4 must go in the middle corner *between* the 1 and 2, and that in turn determines what goes between *them*.

1		
8		
4	7	2

Now the other two rows must also total 13, so the 1 needs 12 and the 2 needs 11, and this is now easy to arrange.

Similar arguments will produce other solutions.

After these problems, the more familiar problem of magic squares will now be fairly easy. An order-3 magic square requires the numbers from 1 to 9 to be placed in a square so that each row and each column, and the two diagonals, sum to the same total.

As before, the important thing is the total of the numbers from 1 to 9, 45, which indicates that each row or column sums to 15. It will be useful to discuss the equivalence of the various solutions, which are rotations or reflections of each other. For example:

8	3	4
1	5	9
6	7	2

4	9	2
3	5	7
8	1	6

8	1	6
3	5	7
4	9	2

SUMMARY AND SUGGESTIONS

What we have done here is to present a variety of situations which focus attention on both the **properties** of numbers and the **relationships** between them.

The ideas involved are mainly to do with **sets of multiples**. The more familiar odd and even numbers are now seen in this more general context, so that even numbers are viewed as multiples of 2. Some sets of multiples are included in others, so that for instance any multiple of 6 is also a multiple of 3. Intersections of these sets develop further ideas about the relationships, so that if we want numbers which are multiples of both 4 and 6, these will be multiples of 12. (A sophisticated extension of this is the idea of 'lowest common multiple'; this was once considered to be a prerequisite for the addition and subtraction of fractions, which needed a 'lowest common denominator'.)

The 100 square in particular relates multiples to **place value**, and raises some questions about why even numbers end in even digits, and what the relationship is between the tens and units digits for, say, multiples of 4.

These ideas could be extended to tests for **divisibility**. How does one recognise a multiple of 10, or 5, or 4, or 8? What is special about multiples of 3 or 9?

Related to this could be a study of **prime numbers**.

Several ideas can be **generalised**, such as the simple one that the sum of an odd and an even number is odd. This can have a **proof** based either on something pictorial, or on some **algebraic notation**. More algebra is possible in the 100 square activity leading to **directed numbers**.

Above all, what is constantly required is a **logical approach** to everything, in which **hypotheses** are formed, tested, and proved and formalised, or rejected and re-formed.

DEVELOPMENT AND DIFFERENTIATION

All the activities can be tackled by children at different levels. At the very least, they can approach problems by trial and error with a great deal of computational practice. (Unlike in more formal activities, the children who need most practice at computation get more of it!) But in doing so they will develop some intuitive ideas about number, and gradually inform their trials with some logical thinking.

Their explanations will depend to some extent on their verbal abilities, and continual discussion will encourage them to explain their ideas, as well as listen to the explanations of others, and to develop a critical and evaluative attitude towards what they hear.

Explanations will be verbal, practical and pictorial. Some will be about particular cases; others will be generalisations of situations. The generalisations may be inductive, extending the particular cases by assuming that they will always be true. Some generalisations will be logically worked out.

Some children will use more sophisticated notation to describe their generalisations. They may invent their own notation, or accept the more conventional use of letters as in algebraic notation. Sometimes the notation will be used in order to prove things in a more formal way.

Such generalisations can start in a simple way with odd and even numbers. One possible notation is to use a box for 'any number': $\square$. An even number is 2 times some number, so we can write it as $2 \times \square$. An odd number is 1 more or 1 less than an even number, so it is $2 \times \square + 1$, or $2 \times \square - 1$.

More conventionally we can use the letter n to stand for 'some number', and an even number is then $2 \times n$. (One can easily introduce at an appropriate time the convention that the multiplication sign is omitted between a number and a letter.) An odd number is then $2n + 1$ or $2n - 1$.

In the situation with the red, yellow and blue cubes, the numbers were respectively $3n + 1$, $3n + 2$ (or $3n - 1$) and $3n$.

If we wish to go further with algebra, then we can play with some equations.

To show odd + odd = even, we can write:

$$(2n + 1) + (2m + 1) = 2n + 2m + 1 + 1$$
$$= 2(n + m) + 2$$

This is obviously even, because twice $(n + m)$ is even, and 2 more is still even.

Or, $2(n + m) + 2 = 2(n + m + 1)$, which is even.

To show that red + yellow = blue, we can write:

$$(3n + 1) + (3m + 2) = 3n + 3m + 1 + 2$$
$$= 3(n + m) + 3$$

This is a multiple of 3.

Alternatively, the yellow can be represented by $3n - 1$, and:

$$(3n + 1) + (3m - 1) = 3n + 3m + 1 - 1$$
$$= 3(n + m)$$

A nice development of the Venn diagrams for sets of multiples is to work with four sets. This does not add much difficulty to the placing of the number tablets, but it is a challenging exercise to try to draw the diagram!

The L-shaped puzzle can vary in size.

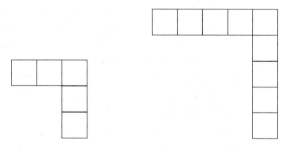

This gives an opportunity for a development of a pattern for the increasing sizes, which in turn depends on the totals for the sum of the first so many numbers. In order to encourage a generalisation of a rule for this, we have already asked for ways of adding the numbers from 1 to 9. If we ask instead for the sum of the numbers from 1 to 100, children are almost forced into finding a method which is quicker than adding the numbers one by one, and on the basis of their earlier experience they will probably think of pairing the first and the last, and so on: 100 + 1, 99 + 2, 98 + 3, ... Each pair adds to 101, and there are 50 pairs, so the total is 50 × 101.

Now what about the sum from 1 to 101? Using the same procedure, each pair adds to 102. But how many pairs are there?

Well, still 50, but there is one number left over. Which one? It is fairly easy to see that it is 51, but it is useful to decide why it is so, and how in general you would work out which is the 'middle' number when the number of numbers is odd.

This gives separate rules for sums of an odd and of an even number of numbers, which is a little inelegant!

A more sophisticated approach is to write:

$$
\begin{aligned}
\text{sum}(100) &= 1 + 2 + 3 + \ldots + 98 + 99 + 100 \\
\text{sum}(100) &= 100 + 99 + 98 + \ldots + 3 + 2 + 1 \\
\text{twice sum}(100) &= 101 + 101 + 101 + \ldots + 101 + 101 + 101 \\
&= 101 \times 50 \\
\text{so sum}(100) &= (101 \times 50) \div 2
\end{aligned}
$$

This can now be generalised:

$$
\begin{aligned}
\text{sum}(n) &= 1 + 2 + 3 + \ldots + (n-2) + (n-1) + n \\
\text{sum}(n) &= n + (n-1) + (n-2) + \ldots + 3 + 2 + 1 \\
2 \times \text{sum}(n) &= (n+1) + (n+1) + (n+1) + \ldots + (n+1) + (n+1) + (n+1) \\
&= (n+1) \times n \\
\text{so sum}(n) &= \frac{(n+1) \times n}{2}
\end{aligned}
$$

There are magic squares of higher order: 4 by 4, 5 by 5, etc.

Here are other puzzles in which all rows must add to the same total, which are more difficult.

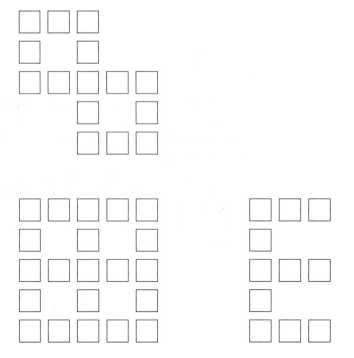

CHAPTER 8

ALGEBRAIC IDEAS

This chapter is essentially about number sequences and how they behave, but in a practical context. There are many simple practical or visual situations which lead to patterns of numbers, which can be recorded in tables. It seems natural to ask what the rule is for such patterns. A rule can be developed in different ways, eventually leading to a verbal generalisation, which can then be recorded symbolically.

PONDS AND PATHS

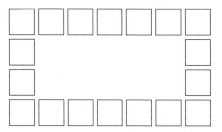

The problem of laying a path round a rectangular pond is an old one, but has been given a new lease of life by forgetting the old idea of working out the area and looking instead at the number of square paving stones needed.

One approach often used by children is to look at sets of sub-problems. I found one class of 9-year-olds sharing such work. One group was looking at ponds which were '1 times something'. (The units do not matter, and they were working on centimetre-squared paper.)

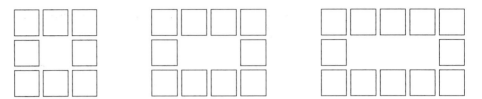

Pursuing this sequence, they drew the diagrams, counted the number of slabs in each case, and put the results into a table

Ponds 1 wide

LENGTH OF POND	1	2	3	4	5	6	...
NUMBER OF SLABS	8	10	12	14	16	18	...

Other groups built up similar tables.

Ponds 2 wide

LENGTH OF POND	1	2	3	4	5	6	...
NUMBER OF SLABS	10	12	14	16	18	20	...

Ponds 3 wide

LENGTH OF POND	1	2	3	4	5	6	...
NO OF SLABS	12	14	16	18	20	22	...

The results of these begin to look remarkably similar, and it is useful to ask why all the sequences increase by 2 each time. (Obviously – to us at least! – each time the pond is made 1 unit longer, it requires another 2 slabs.)
One group worked on square ponds.

LENGTH OF POND	1	2	3	4	5	6	...
NUMBER OF SLABS	8	12	16	20	24	28	...

This produces an increase of 4 each time, and again it is useful to ask why. (Each pond 1 unit larger in length now requires 4 more slabs.)

What happens in each of the above cases if the length of the pond is 10 units?

The number 10 is perhaps too close, because it is tempting for most children merely to continue the sequence until they reach the tenth number. To discourage this, we need to force them into thinking in a different way.

> What happens in each of the above cases if the length of the pond is 100 units?

Yes, they can of course continue each sequence up to 100, but it takes too long! There must be a quicker way.

Let us look at the first sequence again:

LENGTH OF POND	1	2	3	4	5	6	...
NUMBER OF SLABS	8	10	12	14	16	18	...

How does the number of slabs compare with the length? This is not so easy to tell just by looking at the numbers, but children try out various hypotheses.

The 8 is 1×8; the 10 is 2×5; the 12 is 3×4; ... but after that it is more difficult, and the sequence of multipliers has no obvious rule.

The 8 is $1 + 7$; the 10 is $2 + 8$; the 12 is $3 + 9$; ... and it is easy to see that the *addends* increase by 1, but what is the addend for 100? Well, each addend seems to be 6 more than the length, so the addend for 100 is **106**, and if we add this to 100 we get 206. Maybe we can now formulate a general rule: *add 6 to the length, and add the result to the length.* Or, better, this is equivalent to: *twice the length plus 6.*

This is in fact correct, but why is it so? Let us look at the diagram instead of the table:

Where do we have twice the length, and where do we have 6?

Well, if we think about it this way,

now we can see that 'twice the length' gives us the number of slabs above and below the pond, and we always have another 6 slabs, 3 at each end. A similar argument applies to each of the other sequences.

The same argument can be used to go directly to the general case, for *any* size of pond.

> To achieve this, it is useful to ask the children to imagine a pond, say, 10 units long and 8 units wide. How do they count up the slabs?

10 top and bottom is 20; 8 on each side is 16; 4 in the corners: a total of 20 + 16 + 4 = 40. But wait! Rather than add up, it is better to say *twice the length plus twice the width plus 4*, because this indicates how you work it out for *any* pond. Notice in this case how *explaining how you count up* virtually gives you the general rule.

CIRCLES, LINES AND POINTS

Prepare, or ask the children to draw, some circles.

> If you draw one straight line across the circle, into how many regions does it divide the circle?
>
>
>
> Obviously 2.
>   Now, how many regions do you think will be produced if you draw a second line?
>   Well, it depends on where you draw the line:
>
>
>
> The maximum is 4.
>   What about a *third* line? What is the *maximum* number of regions we can get here?

Children often reply '6' to this question. The additive approach is strong, and they see that we have had 2, 4, so 6 comes next. It *is* possible to get 6 regions, but that is not the maximum.

Also, if they consider that before we drew the first line, we had 1 region, then the sequence we now have is:

1, 2, 4 ...

So what comes next? Now they think the rule is *doubling*, so the next number is 8! They try this and can only produce 7:

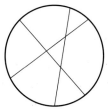

Now it is easier to formulate a new rule for the sequence that begins

1, 2, 4, 7 ...

if they can see that the successive differences between the numbers are 1, 2, 3, ... They can *hypothesise* that the next difference is 4, so the next number in the sequence (the number of regions produced by 4 lines) will be 11. They can add this fourth line, choosing its position carefully, and verify this.

They can of course continue in this way, verifying the result each time. How do they know that the sequence will always obey this rule?

The trouble here is that this situation starts to become too obvious and repetitive. A 'correct' rule has been found very quickly, and it is not easy for the children to see that it still may not be correct.

A more interesting activity is the following.

Draw a circle and mark 2 points on the boundary. Join them up.

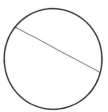

Count the number of regions: in this case 2.

Draw another circle and mark 3 points on the boundary. Join each point to every other point with a straight line.

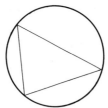

The number of regions is 4.

Draw another circle, mark 4 points on the boundary and join each point to every other point with a straight line.

The number of regions is 8.

Draw another circle and mark 5 points on the boundary. Join each point to every other point with a straight line.

The number of regions is 16.

After such a strong sequence: 2, 4, 8, 16, it is tempting to hypothesise that the rule is that the number of regions *doubles* each time. This is even supported if we go back to 1 point on the boundary, which gives *1* region

1, 2, 4, 8, 16 ...

The next number must *surely* be 32.

But it is not!!

Children will draw and redraw the diagram several times, trying to obtain 32 regions. Sometimes they will get 30 (if three lines intersect at the centre) and sometimes 31, but never 32.

One way to show that it cannot be 32 is to look at the types of regions that are being produced. They come in sixes, with an extra region at the centre. So the number must be 1 more than a multiple of 6, and therefore cannot be 32.

To further disprove the doubling hypothesis, one can also consider the situation where there are *no* points on the boundary, that is, where there is still just 1 region. So the sequence actually begins

1, 1, 2, 4, 8, 16, 31, ...

The rule for this sequence is in fact a complicated one, beyond the reach of primary children. The point of *this* particular exercise is not to find the rule, but to show that it is possible to base a false hypothesis on quite a lot of 'evidence'!

Another situation begins by drawing lines and counting the **intersections.**

      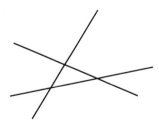

I line, 0 intersection   2 lines, I intersection   3 lines, 3 intersections

The sequence produced is

0, 1, 3, 6, 10, 15 ... .

The differences here are obvious, and after discussion can be explained in terms of the *additional* number of intersections produced by each new line. For instance, the *tenth* line will intersect the 9 lines already there and thus produce 9 new intersections.

One can also count the number of **line segments**, that is, the pieces of line between the intersections.

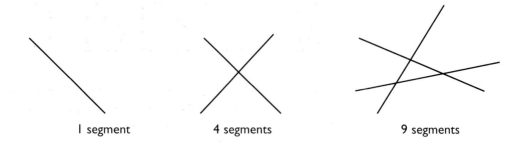

1 segment   4 segments   9 segments

DIAGONALS

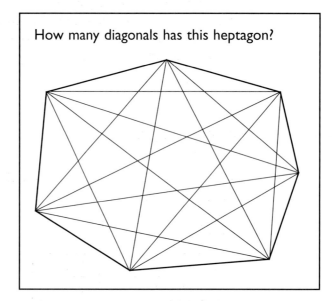

How many diagonals has this heptagon?

It can be provocative to show a diagram of this rather than ask the children to draw it, in order to make it more difficult to count! Even with their own copies of the diagram in front of them, they will find it difficult without marking each diagonal as they count it. But without recourse to this aid, they will find the task impossible unless they try to *calculate* rather than count.

A frequent error is to say: there are 4 diagonals from each vertex, and 7 vertices, and 7×4 is 28. How do they reconcile this with the 14 that they have perhaps counted? Well, working this way, they have in fact counted each diagonal twice, once at each end, so they must divide the 28 by 2.

You may now like to ask the children to work through polygons with different numbers of sides and see how many diagonals there are. They see that a triangle has no diagonals, a quadrilateral has 2, and so on. They can then fill in a table:

SIDES	3	4	5	6	7
DIAGONALS	0	2	5	9	14

They can notice how the number of diagonals increases every time a side is added to the polygon, but it is not so easy to work from the number of sides to the number of diagonals just by looking at the table.

The method of counting illustrated by the heptagon above virtually gives a formula for the diagonals of a polygon with *any* number of sides. We just need to know how many diagonals are at each vertex. Since a vertex cannot be joined by a diagonal to itself, nor to the two adjacent vertices, this will be 3 less than the number of vertices. The rule is therefore: multiply the number of sides by 3 less than the number of sides, and divide by 2. Symbolically this is

$$s \times (s - 3) \div 2.$$

MATCHSTICK CONSTRUCTIONS

The following activities are offered without further comment

SQUARES	1	2
MATCHSTICKS	4	7

LENGTH OF SQUARE	1	2
NUMBER OF SQUARES	1	4
MATCHSTICKS	4	12

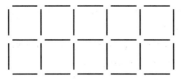

LENGTH OF RECTANGLE	5
WIDTH OF RECTANGLE	2
NUMBER OF SQUARES	10
MATCHSTICKS	27

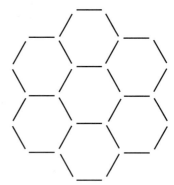

SUMMARY AND SUGGESTIONS

All of the activities suggested in this chapter concern practical or visual situations that lead to **sequences of numbers**. The idea each time is to find the **rule** for the sequence.

Many of the situations are suitable for breaking down into **sub-problems**. You can encourage children to choose these for themselves. Working on sub-problems is an important mathematical strategy to be used when the main problem is too large or too complex. It can also be a way of sharing out work among the class.

The children can of course go directly to the general case in the first place, and imagine what happens and derive any rules from that, without all the preliminary work on separate cases. For instance, it is possible at the start to think about *any* rectangular pond and the number of slabs around it, and come up with the rule straight away. This is a pedagogical point that needs careful thought, and we should consider the following reasons for preceding the general case with particular cases:

1   the preliminary work may be desirable anyway;
2   the experience of it may assist in making the final discovery;

3   it is useful to learn how to break up a problem into sub-
     problems;
4   the filling in of tables is a useful exercise in itself;
5   it is also a good thing to be able to look at sequences of
     numbers and formulate hypotheses about how they are
     constructed.

The results of any investigation can be summarised in a **table**.
The figures can be arranged horizontally,

LENGTH	1	2	3	4	5	6	...
NUMBER OF SLABS	8	12	16	20	24	28	...

or vertically.

LENGTH	NO OF SLABS
1	8
2	12
3	16
...	...

Children usually look at how the sequence progresses in an
additive way. In the above example, the numbers increase by 4
each time. This is correct, but not particularly helpful in
generalising the results. You can ask (as was suggested) how many
slabs will be needed if the length is 100, and hope the children
will be deterred from adding 4s one by one! It does help to
decide how many 4s should be added to the first number, 8.
There will be 99 of them, so the number of slabs for 100 is

$8 + (99 \times 4)$.

This is easier to work out as

$4 + (100 \times 4)$,

and now a general rule seems to be to *start with 4 and add as many
4s as the length*. If the length is 20, the number of slabs is

$4 + (20 \times 4)$.

More generally, if the length is L, then the number of slabs is:

$4 + (L \times 4)$.

However, all this argument assumes that the number sequence
continues in the same way. To be sure of this, we need to look at
the *physical* situation. We can work in two ways:

1   We can look at what happens each time we make the square pond one unit larger. We can see that each time we do this we need 4 more slabs, one in each side of the pond. This supports the additive argument above.

2   We can look immediately at a general case. Whatever the length of one side, we need that number of slabs for each of the four sides. Then we must add the 4 slabs at the corners. This leads to a formulation of the general rule as *4 times the length of the side plus 4.* If the side has length L, then the formula is

$$(4 \times L) + 4$$

which (after appropriate discussion) can be seen to be equivalent to $4 + (L \times 4)$.

DEVELOPMENT AND DIFFERENTIATION

The main feature of the process of looking at a succession of individual cases is that it often involves **counting** – slabs or regions or intersections. For some children this may be a useful exercise, because being able to *organise* the count of a largish number of things is something in which they need practice. For children in general the count may be a deterrent to working out the total in some more efficient way: the counting of the slabs around a pond is typical of a situation in which children merely count around the pond, then put the total in a table, without considering how the slabs are arranged. In all the activities it is a good idea to encourage a discussion of the merits of different ways of counting, and the generalisations that can be derived from them.

Note also that even in a particular case, say for a pond 10 units by 8, saying *how you work out the number of slabs* is a big step in the direction of **generalisation**. To say '10 at the top, 10 at the bottom, 8 on each side and 4 at the corners' is almost a general rule.

It may be a big step from the formulation of such a general rule in **words**, to writing it down in **symbols**. The symbolic representation can of course wait until you think the children are ready for it, and some children may not be before they leave the primary school.

However, the symbolisation enables us to look at some things more easily. The **formula** found for the path around a square pond was

$$4 + (4 \times L).$$

Another way of looking at the path is this

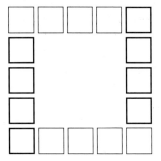

Each of the four strips is 1 more than the length of the pond, so the formula this time is

$4 \times (L + 1)$.

How do we reconcile this with the $(4 \times L) + 4$ we found before?
    One way is to consider the area of a rectangle 4 by $(L + 1)$:

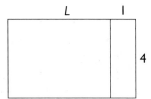

The two rectangles into which it is divided have areas $4 \times L$ and 4, so the total area is

$4 \times (L + 1)$.

If the children find different formulas for the same situation, then similar techniques can be used to show that they are **equivalent**. (Note that this involves things like the traditional 'clearing of brackets' met in textbooks on algebra. It is far more sensible to deal with such manipulation of symbols occasionally, as they occur in situations like this, than to carry out lots of meaningless exercises.)
    The general exploration of **diagonals** can be extended in various ways, as we saw in the 'Strategies' chapter.

CHAPTER 9

CREATING SHAPES

This chapter deals mainly with some combinatorial problems. The activities are concerned with taking simple shapes like squares or triangles and putting them together to make more complicated shapes. A typical problem is to consider how many different combinations can be constructed to fulfil certain rules. This necessitates some systematic way of checking that all possibilities have been found. Such problems also require some clarification by the children of what the rules are, and whether certain combinations are equivalent, so a certain amount of decision-making is required. Usually, equivalent shapes differ in their orientation, and so basic ideas about reflections and rotations will be developed.

FOUR SQUARES

Children are given scissors and sheets of squared paper. (The squares should have 2cm edges or larger.) The children are asked each to cut out a shape made from four squares and write their name on it. Each shape is pinned onto a board. The reasons for writing names on the shapes are first that the creator of each shape can be identified, and second that the intended orientation be recognised.

The children are asked whether any of the shapes are the same.

The phrase 'the same' is purposely vague. The idea is that children will determine what this means.

Some pairs of shapes will obviously be the same because they have the same orientation:

One of the duplicates can be removed as these pairs are identified.
    Other pairs will not be quite so obvious:

Here the children may disagree about whether the shapes are the same or not. They will be different because one is 'upside down', or 'turned round'. A key question is: How can we make the second look the same as the first?
    Answers to this will begin in vague terms: 'Turn it over', 'Turn it upside down', 'Turn it round'. More precision is needed. You can stimulate this with a deliberate misunderstanding of what is said. In each of the following, the right-hand shape above has been 'turned over':

It is important that you do not allow the children to come to the board and show what they mean. If they have to amend their instructions verbally, then they are forced into making them clearer. You can continue to 'misunderstand', or choose to accept something that is unambiguous. One helpful feature may be that in some changes the name written on the shape will move to the back, and in this case that is what is wanted.

The next case is different:

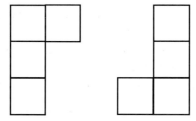

Here the children will probably say, 'Turn it round'. You can still interpret this as a 'turn over', since this is turning it round in three dimensions.

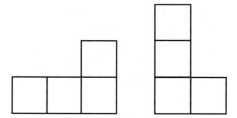

However, if the children explain that it must stay 'the same way up', or that the name must still be showing, or 'you mustn't take it off the board', there is still scope for alternative interpretation.

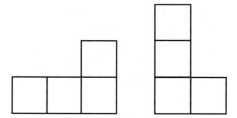

Children may now insist that you turn to the left rather than to the right; but if you turn the top to the left, then the bottom turns to the right, so this is still ambiguous! Perhaps 'clockwise' and 'anticlockwise' will emerge. Or, the instruction will be not to turn it so far, and now the angle of turn can be made more precise, according to what knowledge the children have: quarter turns and half turns are acceptable if they are not sure about degrees.

Two things gradually happen. The first is that children distinguish between a **rotation**, where the shape stays in the plane of the board, and what the Americans call a **flip**, where the shape is taken off the board and reappears as a mirror image of itself. One key to which transformation it is, as has been pointed out, is whether the name written on the shape is still visible or not.

Second, each of these moves is made more precise. A rotation occurs through a certain angle, clockwise or anticlockwise. A flip is about a certain axis, in simple cases horizontal or vertical.

(Note: the relation between a 'flip' and a reflection is slightly difficult. A flip only *represents* the result of a reflection. Physically, the only way of performing a reflection is to use a mirror, and work with mirrors can of course be carried out on other occasions. A reflection is a two-dimensional operation. A flip needs a third dimension in order to reverse the orientation, and in fact is a rotation in three dimensions. These complications need not concern the children at this stage, and they are best left till much later, when they are considering transformations generally in three dimensions.)

The basic idea behind the 'sameness' is that of **congruence**. Two shapes are congruent if one can be put on top of the other so that everything matches.

As various pairs are discussed the duplicates can be removed, until the children agree that all the shapes remaining are different, that is that no two shapes left are congruent.

> Now the children are asked if there are any other shapes made from four squares that they have not yet found.

As further shapes are produced, these are compared with those that were left on the board and checked to see whether they are in fact new ones. Eventually the children may decide that there are no more. Why not? 'Because we can't find any more.'

This now needs some discussion. Just because they cannot find any more, it does not necessarily mean that there are no more. There may be others that they have not thought of yet. How can they be *sure* that they have them all?

Children have had various ideas about this. They can consider that only one shape has four squares in a line:

If a shape has three squares in a line, then there are essentially only two places the fourth can go,

though this, too, will need some discussion.

If the maximum in a line is two squares, then a third square has only one place (otherwise there will be three squares in a line again),

and now the fourth (again with a full discussion) has two possible positions.

Alternatively, one can consider that there are just two possible arrangements for three squares,

and add a fourth square to each of these in all possible positions.

Two observations need to be made about this whole situation.

First, children very often design shapes with squares joined at corners,

or halfway along edges,

or a mixture of these and edge-joined squares, or even shapes made from half-squares:

Naturally, they manage to cut out the corner-joined squares without them falling apart! It is important not to dismiss any of these as 'wrong'. The children can be asked to discuss whether they fulfil the criteria, and as a last resort it can be suggested that they are more complicated to deal with and could be left until later. Indeed, some can deal with them afterwards if they have time and inclination.

Second, there is a more general point. There are in fact five different shapes, and although this is not very many, the course of action which has been described makes the situation sufficiently complex to be interesting, yet not so difficult as to be off-putting. To begin with three or even two squares would be trivial. To start with five squares would present too many possibilities to deal with in this way. As with many other situations dealing with a sequence of increasing complexity, it is important to start *not* with the easiest case, but at the right point in the sequence which is sufficiently challenging.

POLYOMINOES AND NETS

Shapes formed from squares joined edge-to-edge are generally called polyominoes, a term coined as an analogy to 'domino', a shape formed from two squares. So, shapes made from three, four, five and six squares are respectively called trominoes, tetrominoes, pentominoes and hexominoes.

Once the tetrominoes have been found, as above, one can investigate the number of pentominoes in a similar way, except that there is an advantage now in constructing them by adding single squares to the tetrominoes one already has, and removing any duplicates. This is still an exercise in systematic construction, and in recognising duplicates in different orientations.

For the sake of completeness, it may now make sense to go back, so to speak, and verify that there are two trominoes and only one domino.

It is tempting to go on to the hexominoes, but there are 35 of them; and there are 108 heptominoes! Also, sadly, there is no pattern to the numbers as one continues. So it is probably not worth while to continue with polyominoes of a higher order.

However, there is a subset of the hexominoes which is particularly interesting, because they are nets of cubes. One way I have introduced this to children was to ask everyone to make a shape from six squares, and then ask how many could fold theirs up to make a cube. This led naturally to the question of how many different cube nets there were. Apart from the same features that the polyominoes questions had (a systematic method of finding them all, and recognising duplicates), there is an extra dimension to the activity, in more senses than one! Children can, of course, merely design hexominoes, then cut them out and fold them up to see if they are also cube nets. But if they do not cut them out, or if they are setting out to design hexominoes that are also nets of cubes, then it requires some insight into the relationship between the two-dimensional nets and the three-dimensional cubes. Children need to be able to fold up the nets in their minds, so to speak, and this is a valuable exercise in spatial visualisation.

Even without this sophisticated approach, there is still some mileage in cutting out a suspected net, and finding out that one square is in the wrong place. Now some mental imagery is required in order to make the adjustment necessary to correct the error.

SUMMARY AND SUGGESTIONS

These activities give children the opportunity to create shapes from squares in an increasingly **systematic** way. Systems are necessary to create new shapes, to compare existing shapes, and to determine whether all the shapes in any given set have been obtained.

Comparison involves a recognition of **congruent shapes**, in a purposeful way, because this idea is necessary in order to sort out duplicate shapes.

Congruence is a matter not only of sameness but also of difference, and congruent shapes are related by the transformations which change one into another. These are gradually refined as **rotations** and **reflections**. These two ideas are made more precise by talking about the **angle** of rotation and the **axis** or **line** of reflection, and children here are encouraged to think about these ideas mentally. Other work on rotations and reflections, both before and after, can involve more practical approaches.

Cube nets, besides being an extension of the polyomino idea, provide an important example of the **relationship between two dimensions and three dimensions**. The **spatial visualisation** necessary for this activity can be given focus by showing a net for a cube and asking which edges come together, or which vertices come together.

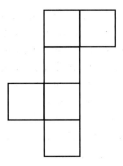

Also, one can show a hexomino which will not make a cube, and ask why not, or more specifically which squares will overlap:

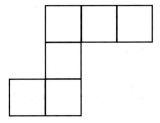

In fact, this last example will fold up to make an *open* cube, but one of the squares is superfluous. So some of the pentominoes will be nets of *open* cubes:

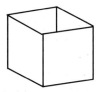

DEVELOPMENT AND DIFFERENTIATION

The first difficult part of the initial problem is that of describing the transformations that demonstrate that certain shapes are 'the same'. If handled carefully, the discussion will involve most of the children, but there will be variation in the degree of sophistication and appropriateness of the language used. As a last resort children can be allowed to come to the board and move the pieces: there still remains a verbal explanation to be given, but the physical demonstration may make this easier.

The most difficult task is not merely finding all the tetrominoes, but *justifying* that all of them have been found. Some of the children will be able to think of ways of doing this. The majority of children will be able to evaluate and criticise the arguments that are presented. All children should at least be able to appreciate something of the arguments being presented.

Similar comments apply to the nets of cubes.

One of the key ideas in considering, say, the adding of a fourth square onto existing three-square shapes, is that of symmetry. If we look first at the 'straight' tromino,

we can see from its symmetry that there are essentially only three distinct places to attach a fourth square:

A similar thing is the case with the L-tromino:

Now we need only note that there is one pair of duplicates produced in this way.

Children who can appreciate the symmetry will be able to use this quicker process. Others will need at least to start by moving the fourth square around *all* the positions about the two trominoes, perhaps gradually appreciating that some positions are equivalent to others, and thereby developing some of the ideas of the symmetries involved.

Two main lines of development are possible from the above situations. The first follows from the principle that whatever one can do with squares, one can do equally well with, say, equilateral triangles. Children find the right-angled nature of square structures easier to deal with, and this is a good reason for starting with squares. The fact that triangles are more difficult is a good reason for continuing with triangles!

Using paper printed with a triangular grid, you can ask similar questions about shapes that are made by joining so many triangles together. You have to start at the right level of challenge, and five triangles may be a suitable number. (NB: we should say *equilateral* triangles each time here, but this should be understood throughout this section.)

Shapes made from triangles in this way are known as **polyamonds,** a term coined analogously from the word 'diamond', a shape made (possibly!) from two equilateral triangles. As with polyominoes, other orders of polyamond can be explored. They have similar names: triamonds, tetramonds, pentamonds, etc. (The names are not important, although the Greek prefixes may be useful in other geometrical contexts.)

The tetramonds are all nets for a **tetrahedron** (or triangular pyramid).

Some of the octamonds are nets for an **octahedron** (a square dipyramid).

Other combinations of shapes can be explored. Hexagons are put together to make **polyhexes**, and these can be explored on a triangular grid if hexagons are not available. Squared paper can be used to explore combinations of 1–by–2 rectangles, and while the right-angled aspect may make this easier than working with triangles or hexagons, the change of symmetry provides a much greater variety: these two shapes are different, but if made from squares instead of rectangles they would be congruent.

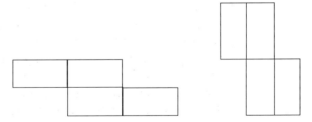

The change from squares to rectangles can be exploited with regard to nets. If instead of looking at nets of cubes we look at nets of **cuboids** (rectangular blocks), then one consideration is how many types of cuboid we can have.

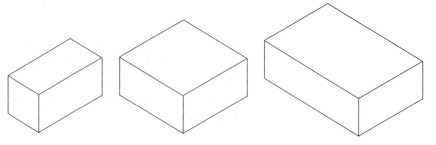

Here, we have two which each have one pair of opposite faces which are squares, and one in which *no* faces are square. A cube has three pairs of opposite faces which are squares.

> Why can we not have just two pairs of opposite faces square?

For each case, the number of different nets can be explored.

If we return to squares, then there are three-dimensional shapes other than cubes which can be made from squares.

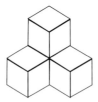

In fact, these are necessarily shapes made from joining cubes together (i.e. **polycubes**), and this suggests another investigation, best explored by using one of the commercially produced sets of interlocking plastic cubes.

There are also commercially produced sets of plastic polygons that join at their edges, and the squares of these can be used for the investigation of polycubes. Joining squares rather than cubes gives an entirely different feel to the exploration. Equilateral triangles can be used for constructing the tetrahedron and octahedron, as well as other shapes made from triangles. But now we are working towards a general exploration of solid shapes made from regular polygons …

Before this gets out of hand, it is worth while emphasising that better problems occur when there are *restrictions* placed on the investigation. A general exploration of three-dimensional shapes, whatever materials are used, is too wide to prevent the creation of a mere random assortment. There may be nothing wrong with randomness as a starting point, and some pupils will quickly start to impose their own restrictions: 'Let's just look at shapes which …'. If this does not happen, you can intervene, preferably by observing what has been constructed so far and asking 'Can you find some others like these?' or 'How many others can you find like these?' Examples have been: shapes made using two different polygons only; two different polygons, but no polygon is joined at the edge to a similar polygon; different pyramids; different prisms; every vertex has the same arrangement of faces round it; shapes which have eight faces.

CHAPTER **10**

PERIMETER AND AREA

I often wonder why such a fuss is made about perimeter.

The perimeter of a shape is the distance all the way round the edge, so it is just another length. Most of the exercises which one sees merely give lengths of sides and ask for the perimeter, so all that is involved is adding some lengths together, and in these days of metric units all that means is addition of number.

Occasionally one meets a formula or two: the perimeter of a square is 4 times its side, or the perimeter of a rectangle is twice the length plus twice the breadth.

The aim of this chapter is to make the topic of perimeter more interesting and mathematically worthwhile, and to relate it to the more important idea of area.

TRIANGLES

We begin with an extension of the idea used in the earlier 'Strategies' chapter, where we fixed the perimeter at 12 units. There we considered shapes made on a geoboard. Here we broaden the scope.

To consider just any old shape is perhaps too broad, so we need to narrow it down. Children, as I have pointed out, can become quite used to formulating sub-problems, and even sub-problems within sub-problems. So, we can decide to look at triangles. And if that is still too broad, we can narrow it down to triangles whose sides are whole numbers.

The first reaction to this problem is often a numerical one. We need three sides which add up to 12, so we can list all the possibilities in order so that we leave none out, and none is repeated:

1, 1, 10	1, 2, 9	1, 3, 8	1, 4, 7	1, 5, 6
2, 2, 8	2, 3, 7	2, 4, 6	2, 5, 5	
3, 3, 6	3, 4, 5			
4, 4, 4				

This looks satisfactory, but it would be an idea to ask the children to draw some of them. This is an interesting exercise in itself. How do you draw a triangle accurately, knowing the sides? How about the 3, 4, 5?

We can draw the 5 first, using a ruler, and perhaps choosing 1 cm as a unit.

A —————————— B

Now how do we draw the side which is 4 units long, attached to the left-hand end? This needs some discussion. One end of the side is at A. Where is the other end? Where could it possibly be, regardless of where the third side is going to be? Ah, it will lie on a circle, centre A, radius 4. Get out the compasses and draw it, or at least enough of it – an arc. Now we can draw another arc, centre B, radius 3, to intersect this one.

Now it does not take long to draw all the triangles, or rather it does not take long to realise that most of them cannot be drawn! Children can then describe what the conditions are on the three sides for a triangle to be possible.

This investigation can now develop in a number of directions.

What about triangles with other perimeters, with whole number sides? Is there a relation between the perimeter and the number of possible triangles? (List the results. Make a table.)

If we look at isosceles triangles with a perimeter of 12, with any length sides, we can look at different lengths for the base. What happens to the height as the base changes? (Measure it. Make a table. Draw a graph.)

If we choose a length for the base of a triangle which has a perimeter of 12, where will the opposite vertex be? (Stretch a loop of string of length 12, round drawing pins placed at the ends of the base and draw all possible positions.) How does the locus change if you change the length of the base, or change the perimeter?

The last paragraph in the above activity is a well known method for drawing ellipses, and the pupils will notice how the shape of the ellipse changes.

If the triangle is right-angled, how can the hypotenuse (the longest side) change? (Use string again. Keep the right angle fixed, and draw in different positions of the hypotenuse.)

The lines when drawn in will produce a curve similar to those produced by curve stitching.

COMPACTNESS

In the last chapter we considered the construction of tetrominoes, shapes made by joining four squares together edge to edge. The areas of them are obviously all the same. But the perimeters vary. Most of them have a perimeter of 10:

This one has a perimeter of 8:

This last one is more **compact** than the others. The squares are, in a sense, closer together.

Looking at it another way, if we had to fence off an area equivalent to 4 squares, then the most compact case would use the least amount of fencing.

One way to look at this problem more generally is to investigate different numbers of squares, in order, and see how compact we can make them. We have little choice over the first few, and it makes little difference whether we choose the L-shaped tromino or the straight one. As we have seen, the square tetromino is the choice for four squares.

The idea seems to be to have squares touching as many other squares as possible, and the sequence can continue like this:

At this stage it does not seem to matter where the seventh square goes,

and we can add an eighth square to either:

But now, in order to have minimum perimeter, the ninth square has to be added to the first of these, not to the second:

As the investigation continues, children will find how crucial the squares are.

Some other interesting things crop up. We noticed above that 8 squares could be arranged just as compactly as a 2-by-4 rectangle, or as a 3-by-3 square with a corner missing. In the same way, 15 squares can be arranged as a 3-by-5 rectangle, or a 4-by-4 square with a corner missing

This is obviously something special about all numbers which are 1 less than a square number.

What happens with shapes made from equilateral triangles? (Use the triangle as a unit of area. There is nothing sacred about squares: it is just that in most cases they are more convenient.)

If we want to **measure** how compact we are getting, then what we can do is look at the **ratio** of perimeter to area.

The tetrominoes with which we started have a ratio of either $10 \div 4 = 2.5$, or (for the square one) $8 \div 4 = 2$. For the square, then, the ratio is smaller, so we are using less 'fencing' for our 4 squares.

We can work out the ratios for the subsequent shapes in our investigation, and we can notice that as the shapes get larger, the ratios generally become less.

If we just look at increasing square arrays, a table summarises what happens with them:

PERIMETER	4	8	12	16	20	24
NO. OF SQUARES	1	4	9	16	25	36
RATIO	4	2	1.3	1	0.8	0.7

We can look at a similar investigation of rectangles, by fixing the perimeter. A perimeter of 26 would give us several rectangles with whole number sides, and we can put these into a table with corresponding areas:

LENGTH	1	2	3	4	5	6	7	8	9	10	11	12
BREADTH	12	11	10	9	8	7	6	5	4	3	2	1
AREA	12	22	30	36	40	42	42	40	36	30	22	12

There is a nice symmetry to the results (which the pupils can explain), and this suggests that the maximum area will be in the middle of the range, when the length and breadth are both 6.5, and the rectangle is a square, and the maximum area is therefore 42.25.

Alternatively, you can fix the area of the rectangle, and look at different perimeters, and also see that the maximum area occurs when the rectangle is a square.

SOME FENCING PROBLEMS

These problems can be tackled on squared paper. Trial and error is a good method to start with. Draw different positions for the fencing and count the squares. Tabulation will increase the level of sophistication.

A farmer has 40 metres of fencing. What is the largest rectangular enclosure he can make?

He is able to use a wall as one side of his enclosure, and use the 40 metres of fencing for the other three sides. How can he enclose the maximum area now?

He is able to use two walls at right angles for two sides of the rectangle…

He now wants an enclosure on the *outside* of a walled right angle, like this:

He wants to build a triangular enclosure against one wall:

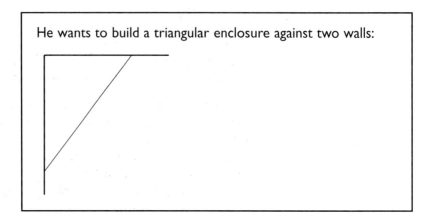

He wants to build a triangular enclosure against two walls:

SUMMARY AND SUGGESTIONS

A focus on the perimeter of triangles produces a surprising number of interesting problems. The choice of 12 as the perimeter of triangles whose sides are whole numbers gives just the right amount of variety to make an **ordered listing** of the number of possible triangles a challenge for most children, but other perimeters could also be investigated.

Once we have realised that the sum of two sides of the triangle must be longer than the third, we can translate this into a numerically equivalent statement, that the largest side must be less than half the perimeter. So, when ordering the number of possible triangles, it might be better to start with the largest possible side.

Going through the possibilities in order of perimeter in fact produces some surprising results:

3: 111
4: *no possibilities!*
5: 221
6: 222
7: 331, 322

8: 332
9: 441, 432, 333
10: 442, 433
11: 551, 542, 533, 443
12: 552, 543, 444

The **construction** of the triangles is obviously an important step in recognising the important relationship between the sides. The general idea can also come from putting together geometric strips or other Meccano-like material, where the impossibility for some lengths can readily be seen:

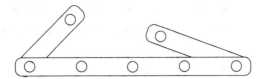

However, the accurate construction of triangles is an important topic in itself, and using compasses in this way is a good introduction to it.

Some of the other questions about triangles involve **relationships** between different lengths. The relationship of height to base of an isosceles triangle needs some initial accurate drawing and measuring to be done in order to obtain some results which can be tabulated:

BASE	1.0	2.0	3.0	4.0	5.0
HEIGHT	5.5	4.9	4.2	3.5	2.4

These results can be put onto a graph:

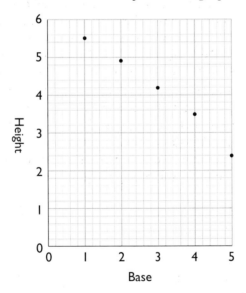

(Pupils may then like to include the cases where the base is zero or 6!)

It is clear that as the base increases, the height decreases, and the pupils can explain why.

The idea of **compactness** is not a recognised topic in the mathematics syllabus, but it leads to some useful ideas about the relationship between perimeter and area. In particular, the **ratio** of one to the other is a useful application of the idea of ratio in a practical context which is purposeful, in the sense that it is being used to determine something about compactness. This has some wider implications which are discussed below.

The compactness issue is pursued under another guise in the **maximisation** problems. One important idea in mathematics is the calculation of maxima and minima in different situations, and the maximising of areas is a very accessible introduction to it.

DEVELOPMENT AND DIFFERENTIATION

There is already enough in this chapter to provide for a wide range of abilities. Most of the activities involve a lot of accurate drawing and counting or measuring. Some of the questions involve properties of numbers. Much is to do with ordering possibilities, and with the tabulation of results. If the pupils know how to draw coordinate graphs, then these can be put to good use whenever a table is concerned with the relationship between two sets of numbers.

The ideas about maximising area for a given perimeter become more applicable when considered in one dimension higher, i.e. when we look at **surface area and volume**.

Some general discussion can centre around questions like:

- Why is a soap bubble a sphere?
- Why are teapots often spherical?
- Why is a dormouse a different shape from a snake?
- Why are radiators the shapes they are?

The soap bubble is the perfect minimum area/maximum volume solution. The other questions are related to this but are mainly concerned instead with heat transference. If a teapot is nearly spherical, it will lose less heat. In the same way, a warm-blooded creature like a dormouse needs to lose as little heat as possible, but the cold-blooded snake needs to keep cool so it has a greater surface-area-to-volume ratio. A radiator needs to radiate as much heat as possible, so designs try to maximise the surface area.

An activity similar to the perimeters of arrays of squares can be carried out with small cubes (preferably wooden ones rather than the ones which clip together).

Given, say, 24 cubes, what different cuboids can you make? Which have the least surface area? What about 64 cubes?

A general investigation of different numbers of cubes will use and develop knowledge about factors of numbers. It will also begin to reveal that the most 'efficient' shape, in terms of minimum surface area, is a cube, or the nearest you can get to it.

(This corresponds to the efficiency of the square in two dimensions when we were putting squares together.)

The problem of perimeters and areas of squares of different sizes can also be transformed to one dimension higher. Work out the surface areas of **cubes** of increasing sizes, and find the ratio of these to the volumes.

Tabulated results will begin to look like this,

EDGE	1	2	3	4
SURFACE AREA	6	24	54	96
VOLUME	1	8	27	64
RATIO	6	3	2	1.5

and it can be seen that the ratio decreases as the size of the cube increases. That tells us that larger teapots are more efficient than small ones in terms of heat loss! Or, it explains why a dormouse is nearly spherical but an elephant is not.

Brighter pupils will perhaps be able to work out the formula for a general case, for both the squares and the cubes.

A square of side s has a perimeter of $4s$ and an area of s^2, so the ratio of perimeter to area is

$$\frac{4s}{s^2} = \frac{4}{s},$$

so as s increases, the ratio becomes smaller.

A similar formula for cubes of side s is

$$\frac{6s^2}{s^3} = \frac{6}{s}.$$

A final problem, which has something in it for all abilities, is the well known 'box' problem.

An open box is to be made by cutting the corners from a sheet of A4 paper and folding up the edges

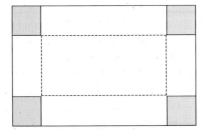

What is the maximum volume possible for the box?

CHAPTER 11

USING CALCULATORS

This chapter describes some activities with simple four-function calculators. It is essential for some of them that the calculators have automatic constant on at least multiplication and division, which most calculators do have*.

The calculators are used here to present problems which either go more deeply into existing ideas about numbers and operations on them, or develop new ideas.

Some of the problems lead to calculator **algorithms**, that is, procedures for using the calculator which are analogous to pencil-and-paper algorithms. Some of the algorithms are of the 'guess and improve' type. The important thing is that they are procedures which are invented by the children themselves.

Note that there are two ways of proceeding. In some activities either all the children have calculators or they share one between two; the sharing obviously means that only one of the pair can operate the calculator at a time, but ⌐urages some discussion between them. In other s only the teacher has a calculator, but offers to e anything with it that the class wants. This means ⌐siderable discussion takes place among the children decide what is the best course of action at any stage. ⌐neans that the teacher can hear this discussion and ⌐ows what ideas the children have. One disadvantage idual calculator work is that it is very difficult for the to know what is going on!

CALCULATORS

---

* To check automatic constant on multiplication, press '3, ×, =': you should get 9. And from '3, ÷, =' you should get 0.3333333.

DOUBLING AND HALVING

DF: What do you get if you double three?

Children: *Six.*

DF: And if you double it again?

Children: *Nine.*

No, it does not always happen. But it has happened many times with groups of 10-year-olds.

Now watch what happens when a calculator is used. I asked a class of 9-year-olds to enter 7 on their machines, and then double it. I had a brief word with those who obtained 77! Everyone else had 14, but they all arrived at it by *adding on* 7.

I asked if there was any other way of turning 7 into 14, and several suggested 'timesing by 2'. We actually tried both methods to double various numbers, counting key-strokes to see which was quicker, but I am not sure whether this made them feel that doubling had anything to do with multiplication.

I asked them to enter 10, and then to halve it. They all *subtracted* 5!

I asked them to enter 11, and then to halve it, and they decided it could not be done!

I gave up this idea, and instead asked them what they had to double to get 12. They knew it was 6.

I asked them what they had to double to get 56. This took longer. Some began by trying various numbers, doubling them to see if they got 56. One pair of boys doubled 25 to get 50, decided they needed another 3 to get the extra 6, and so doubled 28. Two girls (I suspect, unfortunately, prompted by their teacher) calculated 56 ÷ 2.

D S Fielker 'Which operation? Certainly not division!' in *For the Learning of Mathematics*, Quebec, November 1986

The characteristic of the calculator in the above account is that it makes operations *explicit*. The thing about doubling is that children do it in their heads, and are perhaps not aware of which operation they are using. The calculator forces them into a choice: do they add, or multiply? Discussion will reveal these alternatives.

Halving for some children is another thing that they do automatically (if they can) without considering which operation is used. It is particularly difficult to persuade some of them that in order to halve a number by subtracting half of it, you need to know the answer in advance! At least halving 56 presented a problem that they could not do this way, but by then I had already transformed the halving problem into the **inverse** of a doubling problem.

This idea of inverses is an important one throughout mathematics. The children saw that subtracting was the inverse of adding. Now, if doubling is seen as multiplying by 2, halving can be seen as dividing by 2.

In the lesson described above, I subsequently gave the class several higher numbers to halve, and eventually I slipped in 729. Trial and error by doubling different numbers led to the situation where 364 was too small and 365 was too big! However, the two girls who had been led into dividing by 2 by their teacher divided 729 by 2 and got 364.5. They did not know what this meant, but they knew that if you doubled it you got 729!

FINDING FACTORS

> 'Watch me carefully. I am going to enter a whole number in my calculator ... and multiply it ... by another whole number ... and I get 91. Oh dear! Now I have forgotten what the two numbers were. Can you find out for me?'

A first suggestion is usually 1 and 91, and I admit that I can at least remember it was not those two! One discussion proceeded slowly thus (they are all children's comments):

> **'Was it 2 times something?' 'No, if it was 2 times something you'd get an even number.' '3 times something, then.' 'OK. Let's try ... ' 'No, it can't be 3 times something, because 3 thirties is 90, and the next one is 93.' '4 times something ... no, that would be even.' '5 times ... ' 'No, 5 times something gives you a 5 at the end.' 'Or a nought.' '6 times ... no, that's even.' '7 times something. Yeah, maybe.' '7 tens are 70. So 7 elevens are 77. 12 sevens ... that's even. Try 13 times 7.'**

That was an occasion when I alone had a calculator, but I then gave one to everyone and asked them to explore, in the same way, numbers like 187, 111, 161. Eventually they said, 'This is easy; give us something harder!' I asked therefore how I could make it harder, and they replied that I could use larger numbers, or else multiply three numbers together.

I then let them make up problems for each other, which is easy enough to do, since they just have to multiply two numbers and give the calculator with the result on it to their partners. However, *I* was careful always to multiply two *prime* numbers, since this gave a unique answer. If one instead multiplies, say, 6 by 13 and gets 78, then other possible pairs of factors are 3 and 26, and 2 and 39. This is also a situation worth exploring.

SQUARES AND SQUARE ROOTS

DF:	Put 2 into your calculator and press '×, ='. What do you get?
Children:	4.
DF:	What happens?
Children:	It doubles.
DF:	So what would you get if you pressed '1, ×, ='?
Children:	2.
DF:	Try it.

The children do so, and they get 1. Usually they say, 'The calculator has gone wrong,' and they try it again!

Very often it is difficult to surrender a first hypothesis, in spite of the evidence. Eventually they consider other possibilities, and the idea of squaring is expressed in terms of a number 'multiplied by itself'. Now they (well, most of them!) expect '3, ×, =' to produce 9, and so on.

One can ask what is expected from other numbers, and check the results on the calculator. One can introduce the term 'squaring' and discuss why it is called this. One can, now or later, introduce the notation for 3 squared as 3^2.

One can now ask what numbers one has to start with in order to end up with 49; 81; 144; 169; 400.

Next, I can proceed with something more challenging

> 'I put a number in my calculator and press ×, =, and I get 529. What did I square?'

Children can use their own calculators to square various numbers until by trial and error they find 23. But, as suggested above, you will not know what methods are being tried, and what strategies the children are using; and very often the children try numbers at random without any strategy. So it is better for you to use your calculator, and offer to square anything the class suggests, providing they all agree.

On one occasion the discussion centred first on the approximate size of the number wanted. 10 was too small, because it only gave 100. What about 20? That gave 400. 30 gave 900. So the number required was in the 20s. Now there were ideas that it had to end in a 3, because when squared it would end in a 9. 23 in fact gave the right answer. So there are ideas about size, with some mental methods of squaring multiples of 10 and concomitant ideas about place value, and some useful ideas about what is called 'last digit arithmetic'. The last suggestion needs careful handling, of course, because a number ending in 7 will also have a square ending in 9: for example, $27^2 = 729$. (See the 'Development and differentiation' section below.)

Other contributions from children have included the idea that even numbers have even squares and odd numbers have odd squares, or that if you square a multiple of 3 you get a multiple of 3.

Going further with the idea of square roots depends on how much the children know about decimals, and the next activity can be carried out at some other time.

> I tell the children that I square a number on my calculator and get 10. What number did I start with?

Again one has a choice about whether children are left to their own calculators, or whether the teacher with the calculator takes suggestions from the class.

With a bright trio of 10-year-old boys with calculators the solution came very rapidly, accompanied by a joint running commentary: '3 squared is 9 and 4 squared is 16, so it's between 3 and 4. Try 3.5. No, 10 is much nearer 9 than 16, so try 3.1. 9.61. Too small. Try 3.2. 10.24. Too big. Try 3.15.'

I had no chance to stop them and ask about 3.15, but there seemed to be some intuition that this was halfway between 3.1 and 3.2, analogous to 3.5 being halfway between 3 and 4. They continued in the same way, finding 3.16 was too small, 3.17 too big, trying 3.165, and so on, until they arrived at 3.1622777 in about three minutes.

Many 10-year-olds will proceed in the same sort of way, though maybe not with quite the same ease or speed. They do not always follow the systematic procedure of dealing with one decimal place at a time, but this does not matter initially as long as they are developing the general idea of getting closer and closer to the answer. Obviously the class discussion approach is much more successful in sharing ideas about what to do at each step, and allowing mutual criticism and evaluation of the suggestions that are made.

Someone always comes back the next day and says, 'My Dad says all you have to do is press this button,' indicating the square root button. Fine! By now they have the idea of square roots, and it seems sensible to use a more efficient way of finding them. This is not to belittle the trial and error algorithm. For one thing, it works; for another, it is an algorithm that has been *suggested by the children themselves.* Furthermore, as a general principle such **iterative** methods are used in many situations where other methods fail. (See the 'Development and differentiation' section below.)

'THE BIG ONE'

I enter ' ÷ , 31, = ' on my calculator, which automatically programmes it to divide by 31 any number subsequently entered. Without telling the class this, I can now ask them to give me some numbers, and each one is entered, followed by '=', *and nothing else.* (If anything else is entered in between, the calculator has to be reprogrammed.)

On one occasion the lesson proceeded thus

5	0.1612903
9	0.2903225
6	0.1935483
2	0.0645161

DF: OK. What can you say about the numbers we've been getting?

Karen: They've all got nought at the beginning.

DF: Do you think you could get something which didn't have nought at the beginning?

Helen: *Go into double figures.*

10   0.3225806
100   3.2258064

DF: OK. That one starts with a 3. Do you think you could get it to end up with one?

Rachel: *It's got to be between 10 and 100. Try 51.*

51   1.6451612.

Alan: *We've got a one there.*

DF: OK, but can you get one exactly, rather than one-point-something?

The lesson now continued with the children's attempt to get an answer of 1. When they tried

50   1.6129032
23   0.7419354

they knew that the next guess had to be between 23 and 50. They also began to develop ideas about how close they were getting. This was only just over:

35   1.1290322

This was only just under:

30   0.9677419

This was too big,

32   1.032258

but closer than the result for 35.

After a couple of examples as a class, with the teacher operating the calculator in accordance with the class's decisions, the children can play in pairs, each one of the pair setting up a divisor in the same way, by pressing ' ÷ , *their number*, =' and passing the calculator to the other person.

Note the gradual introduction to the aim of the game. Any result will do to start with, then the teacher refines the requirement for the answer. This may be better than insisting right at the beginning that the answer has to be 1.

SUMMARY AND SUGGESTIONS

One of the things a calculator can do is to focus attention on the **operations** being used, that is, whether one is adding, subtracting, multiplying or dividing. This is most striking in the doubling and halving activity, where it is clear that children have thought about these operations in terms of addition and subtraction respectively rather than multiplication and division.

In finding out what to double to get certain numbers, many different mental methods were used, and often these are worth sharing with the rest of the class so that they can be discussed and evaluated.

An underlying idea is that of **inverses**. Multiplication and division are inverse operations, as are addition and subtraction. Doubling is the inverse of halving, and that is why when the actual procedure of halving is not understood (that is, that it is dividing by 2) one can replace the question, 'What is half of … ?' by 'What must I double to get … ?' It is more helpful to see that the inverse of multiplying by 2 is dividing by 2. This can be extended to *trebling*, multiplying by 3, and now we do not have one word to describe the inverse operation, which is dividing by 3. Nor do we have further words for multiplying or dividing by larger numbers. However, following this same idea through with larger numbers helps to put the basic concepts of doubling and halving into a wider context, and raises further interesting properties of numbers (see the 'Development and differentiation' section below).

In the exercise in finding factors, most children, presumably because I say I have *multiplied* two numbers, assume that they have to multiply in order to find the answer. A better alternative is to *divide* the product by successive likely numbers. For example, if the product is 299 one would divide 299 in turn by 3, 5, 7, etc. until the result is a whole number. (One would of course not bother with even numbers, nor with 3 or 5 if one could see that 299 is obviously not a multiple of either.) We can try to stimulate this alternative at the stage where the children are thinking about whether 7 times something is 91: we can ask them how we can find out *how many times* 7 is 91, and this may encourage them to see that, in order to do this, we can divide 91 by 7. Here, then, division is a more efficient strategy than multiplication, but only if the relationship between the two operations is understood.

The relationship between multiplication and division once cropped up in a different situation. A class had been working on the area of a rectangle, and knew that 'area = length × breadth'.

I drew a rectangle, told them the area was 10 and the bottom side was 3, and asked them to find the height. Most of the class set about multiplying 3 by various numbers, trying to get 10, eventually finding that

$$3 \times 3.3333333 = 9.9999999$$

but

$$3 \times 3.3333334 = 10.0000002.$$

It seemed impossible to get anything in between! Only one girl divided 10 by 3 and got 3.3333333, and appeared happy with that! We discussed it with the rest of the class. It seemed to be more efficient than the trial-and-error method.

Another example of the inverse relation is squaring and 'square-rooting'. The idea of **square roots** can really only be introduced as the inverse of squaring.

'The big one' was invented by Hartwig Meissner in Germany in the 1970s, and he was using it with 8-year-olds who initially knew nothing about decimal notation. Yet he found that they were learning about how close numbers were getting to 1, recognising the importance of the digits closest to the decimal point, and identifying for example that 1.093… was lower than 1.123… , and 0.91… was higher than 0.89… . This was without necessarily knowing that the digits after the decimal point represented tenths, hundredths, etc. These are the aspects of decimal notation on which we first concentrate, and we perhaps ignore situations in which children have an opportunity to compare decimals in the way required by this game, and observe whether they are increasing or decreasing, or see how close to a particular number they are getting. Meissner's research showed that this idea of closeness of decimals could be learned independently of decimal place value.

DEVELOPMENT AND DIFFERENTIATION

The choice of **adding or multiplying in order to double** can be based entirely on efficiency. Which takes the smaller number of key-strokes? One class of 9-year-olds looked at this in detail, working out how many key strokes were necessary for different numbers of digits.

No of digits	Adding	Multiplying by 2
1	4	4
2	6	5
3	8	6
4	10	7

The patterns quickly became obvious, and were explained thus. If you are adding, then the number of digits must appear twice, plus the '+' and '=' signs, so it is twice the number of digits plus 2. If you are multiplying, then the digits are entered, followed by '×, 2, =', so it is the number of digits plus 3. One can summarise this as:

No of digits	Adding	Multiplying by 2
n	$2n + 2$	$n + 3$

It is clear that the more digits one has, the more efficient it is to multiply rather than add.

Dividing by numbers other than 2 raises some interesting properties. If one divides by 3, for example, one sees

$$1 \div 3 = 0.3333333$$
$$2 \div 3 = 0.6666667$$
$$3 \div 3 = 1$$
$$4 \div 3 = 1.3333333$$

and so on, so that the decimal parts of successive quotients give the same repeated cycle. One can discuss what these decimal parts mean in terms of fractions, and one can also compare with the properties found in the 'Multiples of three' section in Chapter 7.

Once the children have seen that division is a better strategy than multiplication for finding divisors of numbers, then a useful exercise is to use the calculator to find **prime numbers**. Of course, finding primes up to 100 can easily be done by crossing out multiples from a 100 square, so a nice exercise is to explore primes say between 100 and 200.

Is 101 prime? One can test if it is a multiple of 3 by division, though if one knows that 99 is a multiple of 3 then one knows that 101 will not be. One would not divide by 5, because 101 does not end in a 5 or 0. One would test for 7, and find it does not divide exactly. One would not bother with 9, because if 9 were a divisor then 3 would also be, and it is not. Now one can think about 11: if 11 were a factor then the other factor would be *less than* 11, and we have already tested up to 9.

These are the sorts of considerations that crop up when one considers factors. They are concerned first with relationships between the factors themselves, and second with the idea that one only need test for factors up to the *square root* of the number.

Note that the words **factor** and **divisor** are often interchangeable, and that factor is more commonly used. Strictly speaking, a number that divides into another without a remainder is called a divisor of that number, so that 3 is a divisor of 9. (It is the inverse of **multiple**: 9 is a multiple of 3.) Factors are *sets of divisors* whose product is the number, so that the factors of 24 could be 4 and 6, or 3 and 8, or 2 and 2 and 2 and 3, and so on.

Last digit arithmetic can be explored more generally. As far as squaring is concerned, the results can be summarised thus:

LAST DIGIT OF NUMBER	1	2	3	4	5	6	7	8	9	0
LAST DIGIT OF SQUARE	1	4	9	6	5	6	9	4	1	0

It is now clear that in general each final last digit has two possible origins. It also explains the palindromic sequence of last digits of successive square numbers:

1, 4, 9, 16, 25, 36, 49, 64, 81, 100 ...

and one can also notice that squares never end with a 2, 3, 7 or 8.

The initial problems of **square roots** can also be presented in the form

□ × □ = 16

or as $x^2 = 16$.

Using either notation, one can now present problems such as the following:

$x^2 + 1 = 10$ $x^2 - 5 = 20$
$(x + 3)^2 = 36$ $(x + 2)^2 + 3 = 84$

One can also ask the children to make up their own equations. The above look very much like formidable **quadratic equations**, but in fact the techniques needed to solve them are relatively simple.

Since the **iterative** (trial and error) **method** for square roots also appears to be inferior once the square-root button has been found, it is useful to extend the idea to cube roots, perhaps in the form,

□ × □ × □ = 10

where the same number has to go in each of the boxes. Now, an iterative method is the only way to proceed.

'**The big one**' can be made more sophisticated once the children have grasped the strategy and become more adept at recognising how near to 1 the answers are getting. The teacher can programme the calculator to divide not by a whole number but by, say, 2.7.

On one such occasion the children got as far as

3   1.1111111
2   0.7407407

and there was a sudden realisation that the number required was between 2 and 3! (Note the subtle choice of 2.7 rather than 2.5.) After this, one can choose numbers with more decimal places.

In fact on this particular occasion I was teaching a group of mixed ages, mostly 9- and 10-year-olds but with one 6-year-old. At the crucial point when the number seemed to lie between 2 and 3, it was the *six-year-old* who suggested, 'Try two point five'!! This seems to validate Meissner's work with 8-year-olds.

Iterative methods are useful in other situations. A problem analogous to that of finding factors is for the teacher to *divide* two numbers on the calculator. For example, I divide two whole numbers, and the result is 0.4705882.

(A first suggestion is sometimes $4,705,882 \div 10,000,000$. I make sure that they watch me enter the numbers, so that it is clear they each have a low number of digits!) This is more difficult than the other problem, especially if, as usually happens, children try to explore it by dividing numbers. They generally have some useful ideas, for instance that the first number must be less than the second, or even that it must be less than half the second, because 0.4705882 is less than 0.5. But then they tend to work at random, and an awkward aspect of 'closeness' emerges. For example

$25 \div 53 = 0.4716981$

is very close as far as the dividend is concerned, yet 25 and 53 are far from the original numbers.

Some children have worked through in a systematic way, albeit with considerable discussion

$1 \div 4 = 0.25$ (needs to be bigger, but $1 \div 2$ would be 0.5)
$2 \div 5 = 0.4$ (needs to be bigger, but $2 \div 4$ would be 0.5)
$3 \div 7 = 0.4285714$ (needs to be bigger, but $3 \div 6$ would be 0.5)
$4 \div 9 = 0.4444444$ (needs to be bigger, but $4 \div 8$ would be 0.5)
$5 \div 9 = 0.5555555$ (needs to be smaller, but $5 \div 10$ is 0.5)
$6 \div 13 = 0.4615384$
$7 \div 15 = 0.4666666$
$8 \div 17 = 0.4705882$ Ah!

(An alternative system is to work through successive divisors in the same way.) Apart from the systematic approach, children also learn that to make a number bigger, one must divide by a smaller number, and vice versa. They also develop a quick recognition of when a number will be smaller or bigger than 1/2. Generally speaking, they are building up good insights into decimal notation, and its relation both to fractions and to division.

However, as before this is not the most efficient method, though it is a good idea to go along with it for the sake of all the mathematics that comes out of it.

A better method is to start with the 0.4705882 and multiply it successively by whole numbers

$$0.4705882 \times 2 = 0.9411764$$
$$0.4705882 \times 3 = 1.4117646$$
$$0.4705882 \times 4 = 1.8823528$$

and eventually one comes to:

$$0.4705882 \times 17 = 7.9999994$$

(One can also discuss calculator methods for doing this. 0.4705882 can be entered into the memory, and the 'memory recall' key used to save pressing so many keys each time. Alternatively, entering 0.4705882 and then '+', followed by pressing '=' as many times as is necessary – and counting them – will perhaps be even quicker.)

Now, however, apart from understanding the **relationship between multiplication and division**, it is also necessary to recognise 7.9999994 as 'almost 8', to understand why rounding errors mean that one does not get 8 exactly, and again to use the relationship between multiplication and division to explain that

$$0.4705882 \times 17 = 8$$

is equivalent to

$$8 \div 17 = 0.4705882.$$

Obviously there is a lot here worth discussing!

The **relationship between decimals and fractions** that was in evidence above becomes more explicit in an interesting exploration once suggested by a 10-year-old (see page 60). We had been exploring the squaring function effected by '$\times$, =', and he wondered what '$\div$, =' would do. We began looking at different numbers:

3   0.3333333
4   0.25
5   0.2
6   0.1666666

To the teacher the operation effected by ' ÷ , =' may now be obvious, but to these children it was far from so, mainly because they were not generally familiar with the expression of fractions as decimals. The result was a very long exploration of this **reciprocal** function, finding several of its properties, before eventually getting down to a sensible way of **changing fractions to decimals**. It is easy to say that ⅓ can be converted by calculating 1 ÷ 3, but there were objections to this because

1 ÷ 3 = 0.3333333

yet 0.3333333 × 3 was not equal to 1! They even tried to work out ⅐, not by dividing 1 by 7, but by trying to find what number multiplied by 7 gave 1, using an iterative method:

0.1 × 7 = 0.7
0.2 × 7 = 1.4
0.15 × 7 = 1.05
0.14 × 7 = 0.98

and so on.

As with earlier explorations, this is not the most efficient way of changing a fraction into a decimal, but look at the insights it gives into approximations!

12 DICE AND PROBABILITY

> Probability covers a wide range of topics, and as a part of statistics is one of the most applicable branches of mathematics. We restrict ourselves mainly to dice in this chapter because dice are familiar to children and are cheap and easily accessible, and a wide variety of ideas about probability can be investigated with them.

TWO CONTRASTING EXPERIMENTS

A group of 7-year-olds were playing a game that needed a die. When it was over I picked up the die and asked, 'What's the best number?'

'Six,' they said.

'And how often do you get a 6?'

They thought for a moment, and one pupil said, 'About once every six times.'

'So if I threw this six times, how many times would I get a 6?' 'Once.'

I threw it six times, without getting a 6! 'You try,' I said.

One pupil tried, and got three 6s. Someone else got one 6.

'Now,' I said, 'you all take it in turns to throw the die six times, and one of you can keep a check on what happens, like this,' and I started to record the results on a sheet of squared paper.

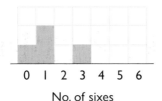

No. of sixes

Children as young as seven can obviously have some useful ideas about probability, and this story illustrates the power of getting their ideas in the first place, in order to develop a worthwhile activity.

One pupil produced a **hypothesis**, that one would get a 6 about every six throws.

Note the subtlety of the question 'So if I threw this six times …' and the subsequent activity. The question already frames a context in which the hypothesis can be tested. The idea of asking two other people also to throw the die six times promotes the idea of **sampling**, in other words that we can test the hypothesis by repeated trials of six throws to see how many of them produce one 6.

In fact the graph eventually showed that in the majority of cases one 6 was produced, thus **verifying** the hypothesis.

Many games played with dice, like Ludo, require a 6 to be thrown before a player can start, so there is interest in how long this takes, sometimes particularly promoted by the unfortunate player who has not moved anything while the others are way ahead! It is always useful to have a discussion beforehand about what the results will show, with children supporting their ideas with reasons.

A second, contrasting experiment can now be carried out which involves throwing a die until a 6 is thrown and recording on a graph how many throws it took each time. A typical result will look like this:

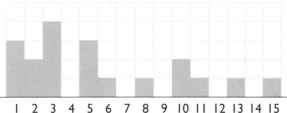

No. of throws taken to get a six

Now the results need to be discussed. Did the experiment turn out as expected? Do all the results show more or less the same thing? How do we regard the 'aberrations'? What do we now expect when we next try to get a 6?

The two experiments outlined here are contrasts because of the nature of the **theoretical** support each can have. The 7-year-olds were able to provide a theory based on the fact that there were six numbers on a die, and each had an equal chance of being thrown. In theory, then, if one throws a die six times, each number would turn up once. In fact, in practice that is most unlikely! What the theory tells us is that 'on average', or 'in the long run', we would expect each number to come up – roughly! – an equal number of times. The relationship between theory and practice is perhaps the most difficult idea about probability, and it needs to be continually discussed as experiments are carried out and observations of results are made.

In the second experiment the theory is not so easy, and it may well be beyond the complete understanding of most primary pupils, but ways towards it will be suggested later. Pupils may have some theories about what to expect. If one expects a 6 every six throws, then one may expect to get a 6 in one of the first six throws; perhaps on average this should come on the third throw. It is certainly not intuitively clear why the *most likely* thing to happen is a 6 on the first throw, as the experiments show.

THE BASIC EXPERIMENT

The simplest experiment with a die is to see whether or not each number does come up the same number of times. To do this you simply throw a die a large number of times, recording what scores you get on a graph. This can be a fairly dull idea, which is one reason why one may not wish to deal with it first, before, say, the more interesting investigations just described.

One way to stimulate interest is to obtain some **biased** dice which are available from some educational suppliers. A few throws by the teacher will probably demonstrate the bias, and then there is more incentive for the pupils to investigate whether their (ordinary) dice are biased, or to inspect the bias of the rigged ones.

Whether or not the idea of bias is introduced in this way, some time early on in their investigation of dice pupils should carry out this experiment on ordinary dice. They expect each number to come up the same, or roughly the same, number of times. The differences from this need to be discussed. There will be differences just because of the nature of things 'in the long run', where the six numbers do come up *roughly* the same number of times, with varying levels of 'roughness'. And there will also be

the aberrations, where one pupil has a completely
disproportionate number of 2s, say – either too many of them or
too few.

Pupils will also bring up the idea of other variables which
affect the result. Does it make any difference if you hold the die
in a different way; always hold it the same way up; drop it from
different heights; spin it as you throw it? They may decide to
restrict these variables in some way. Or they may wish to
investigate the effects of them, singly and in combinations!

*Classroom tip: Ask the children to throw the dice onto a few sheets of
paper: 30 or more dice landing on tables can be very noisy!*

COMBINING SCORES

The **frequency graph** obviously plays a useful part in building up
a visual picture of what is happening as successive experiments
are conducted. This is especially true of the situation where **two
dice** are thrown and the scores are added.

Students should prepare their own graphs ready for the
experiment. They will realise that the maximum total is 12. They
usually automatically start their scale from 1, until they realise
that a score of 1 is impossible!

Total from two dice

They may initially expect equal chances of getting all possible
scores. It is a matter of taste as to whether this point is discussed
in advance, or whether the surprise of getting an uneven
distribution spurs a discussion later. Most graphs will begin to
look something like this:

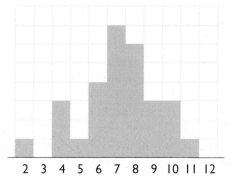

Why is it that more results are obtained in the middle than at the extremes? What do we expect in theory?

How many ways are there of getting a 12? Apparently only one: 6 + 6. Similarly, the only way of obtaining 2 is 1 + 1.

What about 7? This can be 1 + 6, 2 + 5, 3 + 4, ...

Now there is a small problem. Is 3 + 4 the same as 4 + 3? The experience of commutativity of addition is very powerful: of course it does not matter which way round you add two numbers. Yet here is a situation where the difference is important: a 3 on the first die and a 4 on the second, and a 4 on the first die and a 3 on the second, are two different ways of getting 7. Some children will be hard to convince on this point. Sometimes it helps if the two dice are in different colours.

So, there are six ways of getting a total of 7.

Some other minor problems may occur when one considers ways of getting 8. Children will put the possibilities nicely in order again, but start with 1 + 7! The other problem is that having discussed the non-commutativity (so to speak) of the scores on the two dice, pupils may think that there are two different ways that 4 + 4 can occur! This also will need discussion. Then the ways of obtaining 8 can be listed in order

2 + 6, 3 + 5, 4 + 4, 5 + 3, 6 + 2

When the number of possibilities for each total have been worked out, a graph can be drawn of the *theoretical* frequencies.

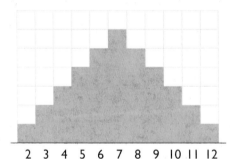

2 3 4 5 6 7 8 9 10 11 12

The next step is perhaps to add the scores of **three dice.** In principle this is not very different from two dice, but the task of ordering the possible ways of getting each total is also a nice problem, different from that of the two dice because the ordering is not so straightforward. For example, the ways of getting 10 are:

1 + 3 + 6, 1 + 4 + 5, 1 + 5 + 4, 1 + 6 + 3
2 + 2 + 6, 2 + 3 + 5, 2 + 4 + 4, 2 + 5 + 3, 2 + 6 + 2
3 + 1 + 6, 3 + 2 + 5, 3 + 3 + 4, 3 + 4 + 3, 3 + 5 + 2, 3 + 6 + 1
4 + 1 + 5, 4 + 2 + 4, 4 + 3 + 3, 4 + 4 + 2, 4 + 5 + 1

5 + 1 + 4, 5 + 2 + 3, 5 + 3 + 2, 5 + 4 + 1
6 + 1 + 3, 6 + 2 + 2, 6 + 3 + 1

Note that they do not have to be put in *this* particular order. The children should be allowed to discuss their own ideas about this, perhaps collecting possibilities at random before they start to organise them.

Eventually a graph can be drawn of these theoretical results. It will be seen to resemble the graph for two dice, in that there are more ways of obtaining results in the middle of the range than at the extremes, and the graph has the same symmetry.

In order to obtain a graph which does not have this symmetry, try throwing two dice and recording the **difference** between the scores. The idea of difference between two numbers may need a little discussion. Normally it is quite easily seen as subtracting the smaller from the larger, but occasionally a pupil with experience of negative numbers, or those who have calculated 2 – 5 on a calculator, will want to distinguish between the difference between 5 and 2 as 3, and the difference between 2 and 5 as negative 3! That is nice thinking, but here we are concerned only with the *positive* difference.

A preliminary discussion of results is always interesting. Pure intuition usually lets you down! The compelling preponderance of 'doubles' prompts a case for zero turning up most frequently, but actual calculation of the possibilities reveals that there are in fact more chances of getting a difference of 1:

6, 5; 5, 6; 5, 4; 4, 5; 4, 3; 3, 4; 3, 2; 2, 3; 2, 1; 1, 2.

Summary and suggestions

It is usually a good idea to let pupils discuss the likely outcome of an experiment before they actually conduct it. The role of **intuition** is important here, mainly because the creation of the theory of probability owes its origins very much to the fact that intuition often lets you down!

The classic case is that of coin tossing. Throw two coins, and what can happen?

1 Both coins land heads.
2 Both land tails.
3 You get one of each.

Intuition tells you that the probability of getting *one of each* is 1 in 3, so 'in the long run' you would expect this to occur one-third of the time. In fact, it will occur about half the time!

Children may be interested to know that the French mathematician D'Alembert made this mistake in 1754 when he was consulted about the outcome of gambling games. In fact there are two ways of getting a head and a tail, because you have to distinguish between the two coins, and so the four cases are:

FIRST COIN	head	head	tail	tail
SECOND COIN	head	tail	head	tail

A sequence for this situation could be:

- discussion
- hypothesis
- experiment
- rejection of hypothesis
- theoretical exploration
- new hypothesis.

As the pupils become more experienced, it will be possible to investigate the theory first, and then verify by experiment a firmer hypothesis based on a theoretical discussion, rather than one based on intuition.

Most of the situations with dice, and the situation with coins, are susceptible to a theoretical treatment. That is, you can work out in **theory** what will be likely to happen, because you can work out all the possibilities, and count up how many ways each can occur.

The question of how long it takes to get a 6 is different, because a theoretical investigation is beyond the reach of most pupils, and the only way to form a hypothesis is therefore on the basis of **experiment**. It is instructive to have other situations where experiment is the only way to see what the probabilities are.

An easy question for the classroom is whether a **drawing pin** is more likely to land point up or point down. Some discussion is necessary to **design** the experiment. It is feasible to throw one drawing pin many times and record the results. Somehow it is more elegant to take **samples** of, say, 10 drawing pins, and record graphically how many times numbers of the sample land point up. This certainly makes a more interesting graph! But it also gives a feeling for **sample size**. Furthermore, as such a graph gradually takes shape, one gets a feeling for how many samples one has to take before one can make any predictions. A graph still looking like this tells very little,

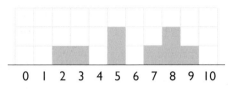

No. of pins landing point-up

but when it gets to this stage, a hypothesis becomes clear:

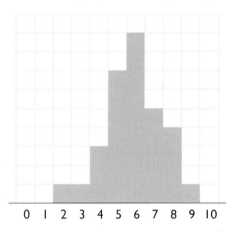

DEVELOPMENT AND DIFFERENTIATION

One important idea in probability is being able to work out **how many ways** something can happen. In many cases this involves putting items into some sort of sensible order, so that you know you have included everything.

The total scores from two dice are a simple example of this. For each possible total you have to work out the number of ways you can get it, and the best way to do this is in a logical order where one score perhaps increases. So, as we saw above, for a total of 7 you would list:

$1 + 6, 2 + 5, 3 + 4, 4 + 3, 5 + 2, 6 + 1$

For the totals from three dice we used a similar procedure, but it was a little more complicated.

For a total of, say, 10 from **four dice** we would do the same sort of thing, and an argument might proceed thus:

$1 + 1 + 1 + \ldots$

We cannot do this because it would need a 7 from the fourth die.

$1 + 1 + 2 + 6, 1 + 1 + 3 + 5, 1 + 1 + 4 + 4, 1 + 1 + 5 + 3,$
$1 + 1 + 6 + 2$

Now that we have listed everything starting with 1 + 1 we can start with 1 + 2:

1 + 2 + 1 + 6, 1 + 2 + 2 + 5, ...

We continue like this, starting with 1 + 3, 1 + 4, 1 + 5, 1 + 6. Then we start with 2 + 1, and so on, in what a seven-year-old girl once called 'dictionary order'!

(Needless to say, working out *all* the possibilities for four dice would be extremely tedious, and the only feasible way of doing it, if you really wanted to, would be to divide the work among the whole class. It is perhaps enough to get the idea by working just on a total of 10.)

There are some diagrams that are useful in determining how many ways things can occur. The **matrix** or **two-way-entry table** will be fairly familiar to most pupils as a way of recording multiplication facts. (It is also used for things like bus timetables.) It can be used for looking at the results of throwing two dice thus:

Second die

First die	1	2	3	4	5	6
1	2	3	4	5	6	7
2	3	4	5	6	7	8
3	4	5	6	7	8	9
4	5	6	7	8	9	10
5	6	7	8	9	10	11
6	7	8	9	10	11	12

Here, the entries are the *sums* of the two scores, and it is easy to see how many times each sum occurs, and why. This also helps to clear up the difficulty of distinguishing between, say, 3 on one die and 4 on the other, and its reverse, and of showing why there is only one way of getting any double.

The entries in the table can be replaced by the *differences* between the two scores

Second die

First die	1	2	3	4	5	6
1	0	1	2	3	4	5
2	1	0	1	2	3	4
3	2	1	0	1	2	3
4	3	2	1	0	1	2
5	4	3	2	1	0	1
6	5	4	3	2	1	0

A similar matrix for two coins will look like this

Second coin
H   T

		H	T
First	H	HH	HT
coin	T	TH	TT

Sooner or later pupils will need to **quantify** the probability of something happening. This can be done first from the experimental evidence, and then from the theory. A 6 is obtained from one die about 'one-sixth' of the time; the probability of getting a 6 is 'one in six'; i.e. '1/6'.

In situations where the actual chances cannot be calculated theoretically, the probabilities have to be deduced from the evidence. Drawing pins may land point up about 'half' the time, or '50 per cent' of the time. Since by now the pupils will know that experimental evidence only corresponds to the theory approximately, some **approximation** is necessary, so there is scope for this, and for some flexibility between fractions, percentages and decimals.

A disadvantage of the two-way-entry table is, naturally, that it only works for combining two sets of events, like two dice or two coins. For three dice we need a **tree diagram**. This works as follows. We begin with the possibilities for the first die:

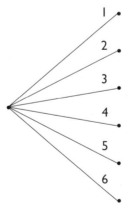

Now for each branch of the tree we have to attach branches for the second die:

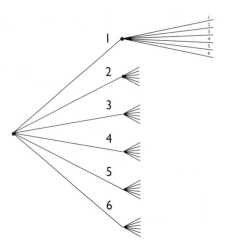

So far we have results for two dice, and we can label the ends of the branches with the appropriate total scores:

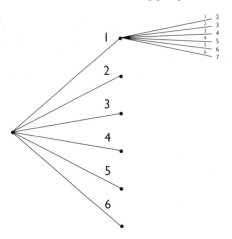

For three dice we would add more branches:

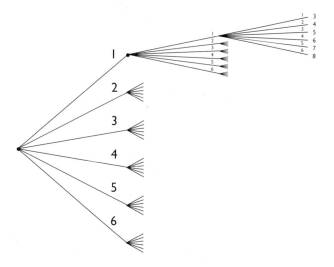

We could also continue with more dice if we wished.

The true advantage of the tree diagram can be seen if we use it to look at the situation where we wanted to know how many throws it took to get a 6. We look first at the first throw:

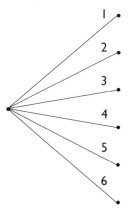

We can immediately see that there is 1 chance in 6 of getting a 6 on the first throw. Then we follow this with the second throw, but the second throw only takes place if we throw anything other than a 6 on the first throw:

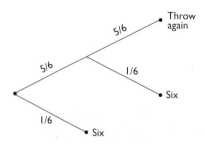

There is 1 chance in 6 of getting a 6 on the second throw, but only in ⅚ of the outcomes of the first throw, so the probability of getting a 6 on the second throw is ⅚ of ⅙, or ⁵⁄₃₆.

How far you can continue with this idea may depend upon how familiar the pupils are with multiplication of fractions. However, it is possible to continue by working on an empirical basis, or even to develop rules for multiplication of fractions from this sort of situation!

CHAPTER

NOT A SUMMARY

I used to end my courses for teachers with a kind of disclaimer. It is customary, of course, to 'sum up' at the end of such an event, but I never did, for two reasons.

First, we had been engaged in a lot of work together. We had shared and discussed new ideas, we had watched children at work, we had wrestled in various ways with bits of mathematics, we had considered styles of teaching, and much more. But each person would have got something different out of the course, according to what they believed in, what stage they were at, how comfortable they felt with any challenges. I could not therefore sum up what had happened to each person: they could only do that for themselves.

The other reason is that somehow a summing up indicates that something has finished: that was your course in mathematics; you have done that, you do not need to do it again. But my view of a course was different: I saw it as just one happening in the series of events that makes up anyone's experiences that affect their teaching. In any case, most of the teachers I worked with used to come regularly to such courses, so they were part of a continual development of in-service education. Part of my philosophy of that in-service education was that I would always meet those teachers again! The implication of that was that we had never finished anything; we had merely enabled each other to get a little further in our thinking, and we would continue the process next time.

Time is of the essence. It takes time to think over new ideas. It takes time to try them out. It takes time to consider their effectiveness for yourself and how they fit into your own philosophy of teaching.

One implication of the necessary time delay is that the process of 'evaluation', which often takes place at the end of a course – usually by the requirement to fill in a form with comments or with ticks in boxes, is completely *mis*-timed. If the purpose is to inform the in-service provider whether suitable things had been done, it was by now too late: that kind of feedback should be ascertained all the way through the course, and adjustments made along the way. On the other hand, if the purpose is to assess the effect of the course on the participants, then it is far too early: the moment at which a course finishes is probably the worst time to make such an assessment.

A teacher once turned up for a course who looked slightly familiar. He reintroduced himself, and said, 'You probably don't remember me. I came on one of your courses about five years ago. I went away thinking you were mad. But recently I have begun thinking about what you said …'.

It is not really feasible to evaluate a course five years later! But for some people it takes so long to have any effect.

So, no summary for this book either. However, This book is not a course. It differs from a course, among other ways, in that you can sample it when you will, dip into it, try out ideas, think about implications, re-read parts of it, use it to suit your own style of learning. What you get out of it will depend upon you, not only in what you do about it, but also in who you are and where you are.

If not a summary, then there are a few odds and ends of things to add. I hesitated to insert a title saying 'Odds and ends', which might have given the wrong impression about their importance. Nor did I want to include a heading like 'Some final thoughts', because the word 'final' might again give some unintended feeling that I was summing up or rounding off! These are final thoughts only in the sense that they are a miscellany of equally important ideas, which happen to be placed at the end of the book. Although there are references to in-service work, they are mainly about what happens in the classroom.

Each of them could easily become a book on its own, but that is not a hint to the publisher! It is an excuse for the fact that they have been expressed very concisely. You may wish to take them merely as stimuli to further thought, just in case you do not have enough to think about already!

GROUPS AND REPORTING BACK

I occasionally would split teachers up into small groups, with a task to work on some mathematics, or to discuss a teaching point, but I never followed such a session with a get-together at which groups 'reported back'. The important thing was what each person got out of the group activity. But reporting back usually consists of reporting some conclusions or opinions, without describing the interesting things that happened on the way and which led to them. There is time for the conclusions, but not for the routes that took a group to them, because that would take about as long as the group took! (As I remarked somewhere else earlier, a similar argument applies to marking written work, which is usually a summary of conclusions to which pupils came, without any description of the process that went on in order to get there. I shall take up this idea in a moment.)

There are many times when you will wish to split your class into groups in order to work at some mathematics or to discuss something. Although class discussions are valuable, for the many reasons given elsewhere, splitting into groups generally enables more children to take part in a discussion, or to contribute to some mathematics, and whenever a class discussion shows signs of being taken over by one or two pupils it is probably time to diversify. Only you can judge, and one must never make the mistake of assuming that children are not participating in some useful way, or getting something out of what is going on, just because they are not saying anything.

However, the same point about reporting back still holds. After a session of group work, the members of each group are mainly interested in what *they* have done and not in what other groups have done. Reporting back may have some benefits occasionally just in the actual exercise of learning how to report back, but again this is of considerably more benefit for the reporters than for the receivers.

A better way of summarising their work for others would be for each group to prepare an appropriate description of what they have done.

RECORDING

Most mathematics that children produce on paper consists of calculations, usually set out as formal algorithms. Rarely are they asked to *write about* mathematics.

When I have taken over a new class, brought up largely on a diet of calculation, one of my first tasks in oral work is to get them to *explain* what they are thinking and doing. This is more difficult than it sounds, when they have been used to giving largely numerical answers, which are met with a yes or a no from a teacher. I rarely give a yes or no, but ask for agreement or disagreement from the rest of the class, who then have to give *their* explanations for why they agree or not.

The next stage is to convert this explanation into *writing*. This is even more difficult. 'What do I write?' they ask. 'Explain to me what you have done,' I answer. This they can perhaps now do. 'OK,' I say, 'now write that down!' But somehow the act of converting the spoken word into the written word is not so easy, especially when you are not used to writing words in mathematics, but only numbers.

Eventually (or sooner with pupils who have been used to this from the beginning), I can say that what I want from them is not just answers but I want to know how they arrived at those answers. If they did wrong things on the way, I also want to know about the errors, and how they recognised that they had made them. I want a full account of what they did, what they thought, what they found out, illustrated by diagrams and tables and graphs as appropriate.

Another idea may also be useful. So far I have described what they are to produce as something which informs *me* about what they were doing. Occasionally, however, the target audience could be someone else. When children are writing something in what they identify as English lessons, they are often given a readership to bear in mind, for whom they are writing. Most times it is naturally for the teacher to read anyway, but apart from that it helps if they know that they are supposed to be writing for parents, other children, the local newspaper, or whatever is appropriate. It focuses their attention on a particular clarity, and it can also affect the style in which something is written. (We ourselves write differently if we are composing an article for an educational journal, a letter to a parent, a notice for the staffroom notice-board, a note to our class, or a book for teachers!)

The same idea could be used in mathematics. Maybe a piece of work is to be written up to be sent to one of those journals for teachers which occasionally includes work by children. Maybe it is for other children to read, perhaps as a display on the notice-board. Maybe it is for their own parents, or for parents in general.

PROBLEM-SOLVING

I seem to have concentrated a little more on problem-*posing*, or at least that aspect has been made more explicit in some chapters.

How you feel about teaching children how to solve problems in mathematics will depend on how you feel about teaching, and how you feel about mathematics, and as I proposed above this will be an ever-developing state. All I have space for here is a brief statement of my own feelings, which was once succinctly put by an ex-pupil I met years later who had become a primary school teacher.

'How do you teach them to solve problems?' I asked him.

'I do the same as you used to do with us,' he replied. 'I give them problems to solve, and then I don't tell them how to solve them.'

CHOOSING MATERIALS

Some problems are based on materials, or are about materials, so obviously you need to start with them. If you are asking how many squares can be made on a 25-pin geoboard then you need to begin with the geoboards.

At other times, materials are used to help solve a problem about something else, and here and there when describing activities I have indicated what materials may be suitable. In this case, as I have also suggested, *choosing which materials are to be used* is part of the problem-solving process.

So that this really is a conscious choice, a choice needs to be properly available. It is not a choice if the dotty paper is already out on the tables, or even if you are holding it in your hand waiting to distribute it when asked. It is not a choice if you have already taken the compasses out of the cupboard and they are waiting on your desk. So, you may have to be more subtle than this about the materials which *you* think the children are going to want, or should use!

Ideally, all the usual materials that children want to use for mathematics should somehow be accessible, both physically and mentally. Physically, your classroom is best organised so that children can easily go and fetch whatever they want. Mentally, the children need to build up an experience of using a variety of materials so that they gradually become familiar with what they can do with them.

'REAL LIFE' MATHEMATICS

It is a popular myth that children will not be interested in mathematics unless they can see a use for it. Most of the mathematics with which this book deals is fairly useless, but it has been found to be enjoyable – like poetry, art or music. This myth has probably been perpetrated by teachers who feel they cannot make mathematics enjoyable!

Some of it *is* useful, of course, but the actual uses to which it is put are usually far less interesting than the mathematics itself! This is probably because whenever there is a really justifiable use, the mathematics involved is either something trivial like routine calculation, or is too complicated for the children to deal with.

The myth has become a myth largely because, in the desperation to make mathematics appear to be useful, it has been applied to a large number of situations where the application is entirely inappropriate. This then has the opposite effect, and convinces the children that mathematics is indeed useless!

In any case, since so many other resources try to emphasise the utility of the subject, I make no apologies for redressing the balance.

Once in a while I find that I can relate a piece of mathematics to something outside the subject, but rather than apply the mathematics to the external topic, it is more a case of deriving some pure mathematics *from* it.

Recently, I walked into my class of 7-year-olds for their weekly lesson of 'enrichment mathematics', carrying the pegboards and pegs that we had been using for the four-in-a-row game described in one of the chapters. I noticed a very large jigsaw puzzle partially completed on a side table that they had obviously been working on since my last visit.

I put down the box I was carrying, picked up a couple of the jigsaw pieces and drew them on the board. We talked about the way the tongues fitted into the slots, and how each piece was made from a square, with a tongue or a slot in the middle of each side. We then became engaged in finding out how many different pieces there could be, in terms of the arrangement of tongues and slots around the square. We put them in order and sorted them in various ways, disposed of duplicates, and decided that there were six types altogether.

Here was a piece of 'real life' mathematics, taken straight from a topic of current interest! I suggested that the following week we could look at the edge and corner pieces, a problem they had already raised.

Oh, they said. Can't we go back to the four-in-a-row game?

INDEX OF MATHEMATICAL TOPICS

halving   131
hexagons 44
hexominoes 44
hypotenuse 122

inclusion 76 et seq
intersection 76 et seq
intersections 101 et seq
inverse   132, 137

kite   45

multiples 62, 75 et seq,
multiplication 37, 48, 79 et seq, 132 et seq, 137, 142

nets   44, 46, 48, 113 et seq

octahedron 44, 117, 118
ordering 29, 89, 121, 126, 141, 148 et seq

parallelogram 45
pentagons 34, 46, 69
pentominoes 42 et seq
perimeter 28 et seq, 38, 64 et seq, 120 et seq
place value 83 et seq
polyamonds 44, 116
polycubes 118
polyhexes 117
polygons 49, 65, 119
polyominoes 44, 109 et seq, 113 et seq, 116
prime numbers 19 et seq, 48, 49, 139
prisms   40,119
probability 38, 144 et seq
pyramids 40, 119

quadrilaterals 33, 35, 38, 39, 68

ratio   64 et seq, 124, 127
reciprocal 143
rectangles 66
reflection 43, 109 et seq
regions   98 et seq
rhombus 45
rotation 43, 109 et seq